TEACHER'S ANNOTATED EDITION
PRACTICE WORKSHEETS
LEVEL 4

TO ACCOMPANY

HEATH MATHEMATICS
CONNECTIONS

HEATH

D.C. Heath and Company
Lexington, Massachusetts / Toronto, Ontario

To the Teacher

Practice Worksheets are linked directly to the lessons in the
Pupil's Edition of Heath Mathematics CONNECTIONS.
Each Worksheet is shown in reduced, annotated form at point
of use in the CONNECTIONS Teacher's Edition. These mate-
rials are designed to provide additional practice to ensure
that students thoroughly master the objectives of the lesson.

Published simultaneously in Canada

Printed in the United States of America

International Standard Book Number: 0-669-30964-8

3 4 5 6 7 8 9 10   POO   99 98 97 96 95 94

1.1 ▸ PRACTICE

Estimating How Many

Mr. Hall's class held an estimating contest. They tried to guess the number of pennies in a piggy bank. The bar graph shows their estimates.

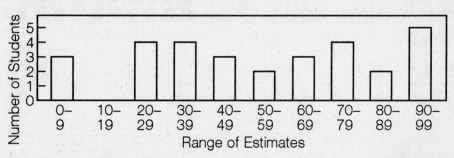

Use the bar graph to answer each question.

1. How many students estimated between 30 and 39?

4 students

2. In which range did the most number of students estimate?

90–99

3. How many students are in Mr. Hall's class? **30 students**

4. How many students are in half the class? **15 students**

5. Did more than or less than half of the students make estimates less than 50? **less than**

6. In which ranges did the same number of students estimate?

0–9, 40–49, and 60–69; 20–29, 30–39, and 70–79; 50–59 and 80–89

7. How many students made estimates below 30? Above 80?

7 students; 7 students

8. How many students estimated between 20 and 40?

8 students

9. How many students estimated between 10 and 19?

zero students

10. Did more students estimate over 50 or under 50? **over 50**

11. In what range does each estimate belong?

a. 25 **20–29**   **b.** 50 **50–59**   **c.** 88 **80–89**

1.2 ▸ PRACTICE

for pages 4–5

Using Tens to Estimate

Estimate how many are in each picture. Circle each estimate.

1. △△△△△△△△△△△△△△
   △△△△△△△△△△△△△

| 15 | (25) | 50 |

2.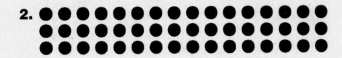

| 25 | (50) | 80 |

3. ☆☆☆☆☆☆☆☆☆☆☆☆☆☆
   ☆☆☆☆☆☆☆☆☆☆☆☆☆☆
   ☆☆☆☆☆☆☆☆☆☆☆☆☆

| 20 | 40 | (60) |

4. ➤➤➤➤➤➤➤➤➤➤➤➤➤➤
   ➤➤➤➤➤➤➤➤➤➤➤➤➤

| 50 | (100) | 200 |

5. ○○○○○○○○○○○○
   ○○○○○○○○○○○○
   ○○○○○○○○○○○

| (45) | 60 | 80 |

6. ▭ ▭ ▭ ▭ ▭ ▭
   ▭ ▭ ▭ ▭ ▭ ▭

| (10) | 20 | 30 |

7.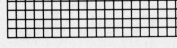

| 50 | (90) | 110 |

8.

| 75 | (150) | 230 |

9.

| 70 | 100 | (200) |

1.3 PRACTICE

for pages 6–7

Mental Math: Using Facts

Write the answer.

1. 30 + 20 = __50__ H

2. 1500 − 800 = __700__ Y

3. 200 + 400 = __600__ I

4. 5 + 8 = __13__ E

5. 140 − 50 = __90__ I

6. 16 − 8 = __8__ R

7. 40 + 50 = __90__ I

8. 80 + 90 = __170__ O

9. 140 − 80 = __60__ T

10. 1200 − 800 = __400__ T

11. 700 + 400 = __1100__ A

12. 5 + 6 = __11__ C

13. 130 − 70 = __60__ T

14. 12 − 5 = __7__ N

15. 80 − 40 = __40__ D

16. 40 + 10 + 30 = __80__ I

17. 20 + 40 + 60 = __120__ N

18. 30 + 30 = __60__ T

19. 100 + 300 = __400__ T

20. 1600 − 900 = __700__ Y

21. 130 − 90 = __40__ D

Write the letter above each sum to answer the riddle.

Where does Friday come before Thursday?

I	N		T	H	E		D	I	C	T	I	O	N	A	R	Y
600	7		60	50	13		40	90	11	400	80	170	120	1100	8	700

Write each pair of numbers that have a sum of 10.

1	4	6	9
3	7	2	8

1 + 9; 2 + 8; 3 + 7; 4 + 6

Write each pair of numbers that have a sum of 10,000.

8000	9000	3000	6000
4000	2000	1000	7000

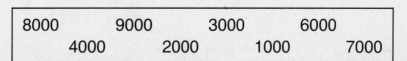

1000 + 9000; 2000 + 8000; 3000 + 7000; 4000 + 6000

1.4 ▶ PRACTICE

Problem Solving: **Problem Solver's Guide**

Solve each problem. The Problem Solver's Guide may help.

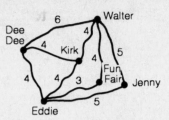

1. Dee Dee and 4 of her friends are going to the Fun Fair. What is the shortest route from Dee Dee's house to each of her friends' houses and then to the fair?

   Dee Dee, Kirk, Walter, Jenny, Eddie, Fun Fair

2. At the fair, Kirk knocks over pins at the Knockoff Booth. Which pins must Kirk knock over to win the grand prize?

   6–8–10 or 10–12–2

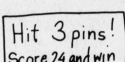

3. How many different ways can you knock over pins and get a score of 18? **three (2–6–10, 8–10, 12–6)**

4. The 36 balloons at the Pop-It Booth are set up in a pattern. There are 2 balloons of each color in each row. Look at the board after Jenny played. How many red balloons did Jenny pop?

   6 red balloons

5. Eddie tries to answer a question asked by "Mr. Know-It-All." Eddie is asked what is the least number of cans he would need if he were building a pyramid 5 rows high and no two rows could have the same number of cans. What is Eddie's answer?

   15 cans

6. The five children want pizza for lunch. Each child wants at least 2 slices. What should they buy to spend the least amount of money?

   They should buy 1 large pie and 2 single slices

   for a cost of $6.75.

Mama Mia Pizza	
Slice	75¢
Small Pie (5 slices)	$3.50
Large Pie (8 slices)	$5.25
Xtra Large Pie (10 slices)	$7.50

1.5 ▸ PRACTICE

for pages 10–11

Place Value—Hundreds and Thousands

Use the clues to complete the puzzle. Each clue gives a number in word form or expanded form. Write that number in standard form in the correct boxes.

```
        A1  4  8  B2
                  3        C6  2  D5
              E1  0  6  F9        0
    G8  H3  9  2        6        0
        0     I7  J6     K4  0  L7  3
        0        M4  7  3     8
    N4  0  5        4        8
    0
```

Across

A. one thousand four hundred eighty-two

C. 600 + 20 + 5

E. one thousand sixty-nine

G. 8000 + 300 + 90 + 2

I. seventy-six

K. four thousand seventy-three

M. 400 + 70 + 3

N. four hundred five

Down

B. two hundred thirty-six

D. 5000 + 3

E. one hundred twenty-seven

F. 9000 + 600 + 40 + 3

H. three thousand

J. six hundred forty-four

L. 700 + 80 + 8

N. forty

1.6 ▸ PRACTICE

Fives and Tens

Label the number line to show the halfway point between each pair of numbers.

1. 30, 40

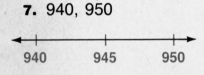

2. 500, 600

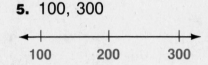

3. 2000, 3000

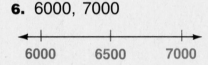

4. 390, 400

5. 100, 300

6. 6000, 7000

7. 940, 950

8. 0, 100

9. 720, 740

Estimate what number the arrow is pointing to.

10.

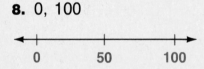

Answers may vary but may include 126–128.

11.

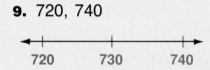

Answers may vary but may include 360–380.

12.

Answers may vary but may include 620–640.

13.

Answers may vary but may include 96–99.

1.7 PRACTICE

Rounding to the Nearest 10 and 100

Round each number in the box to the nearest 10.
Write it in the correct column.

46	71	68	93	64	
	55	74	53	85	
82	37	77	45	59	

Rounds To					
40	50	60	70	80	90
37	46	64	71	82	93
	53	55	68	77	85
	45	59	74		

Round each number in the box to the nearest 100.
Write it in the correct column.

121	231	307	459	250
349	416	127	268	
429	389	450	249	327

Rounds To				
100	200	300	400	500
121	231	307	416	459
127	249	250	429	450
		349	389	
		268		
		327		

1.8 ▶ PRACTICE

Rounding Sensibly

Frank used the fact sheet to write the first draft of an article on the Newtown Forestry Center.

A summer program will be offered at the Newtown Forestry Center. Students about 10 years old will pay close to $30 for the program. It will begin on about July 10 and end on about August 10.

The center was opened on about April 30, 1990. Admission to the center is $2 for adults and $1 for children. This year, 10,972 visitors have toured the center. They saw more than 30 exhibits and about 60 labeled trees. The center is open for visitors from about 8:00 A.M.–6:00 P.M. every day.

Fact Sheet
Newtown Forestry Center
Opened - April 25, 1985

Hours - 8:30 A.M.–6:15 P.M.
Admission - $2 Adults
$1 Children
Visitors this year - 10,972
Exhibits - 31
Labeled Trees - 59 types
Summer Program
 July 7–August 9
 Ages 8–12
 Monday–Thursday
 $26 per student

Use the article and the fact sheet to help Frank write the final version of the article. Round numbers only when it makes sense. Answers may vary.

A summer program will be offered at the Newtown Forestry

Center. Students ____8–12____ years old will pay

____$26____ for the program. It will begin on

____July 7____ and end on ____August 9____.

The Center was opened on __April 25, 1985__. Admission to

the center is ____$2____ for adults and

____$1____ for children. This year, __about 11,000__

visitors have enjoyed the __more than 30__ exhibits and

__about 60__ labeled trees. The center is open for

visitors from __8:30 A.M.–6:15 P.M.__ every day.

Place Value to One Million

Match the expanded or word form of each number in Column A with the number's standard form in Column B. Draw a line from the dot after the number in Column A to the dot before the correct number in Column B. The letters that are not crossed out by the lines spell the answer to the riddle at the bottom of the page.

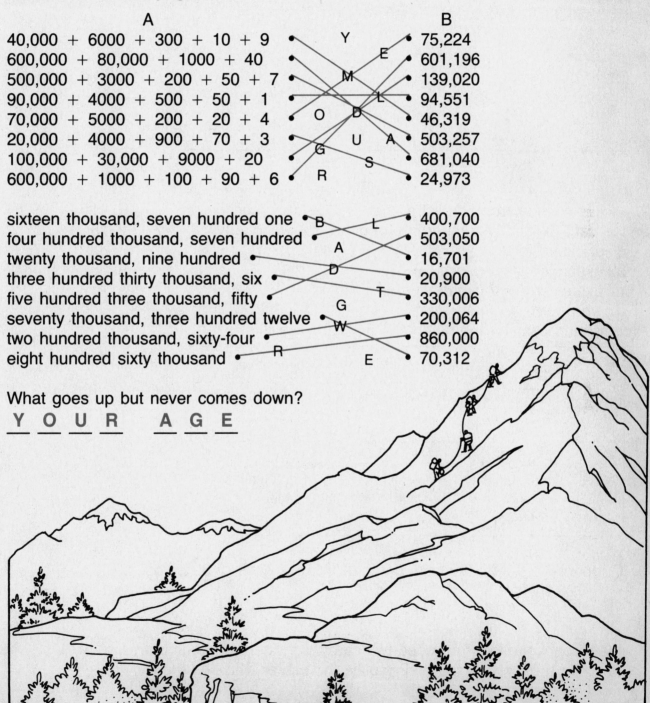

A

40,000 + 6000 + 300 + 10 + 9 •
600,000 + 80,000 + 1000 + 40 •
500,000 + 3000 + 200 + 50 + 7 •
90,000 + 4000 + 500 + 50 + 1 •
70,000 + 5000 + 200 + 20 + 4 •
20,000 + 4000 + 900 + 70 + 3 •
100,000 + 30,000 + 9000 + 20 •
600,000 + 1000 + 100 + 90 + 6 •

Y E M L O D U A G S R

B

• 75,224
• 601,196
• 139,020
• 94,551
• 46,319
• 503,257
• 681,040
• 24,973

sixteen thousand, seven hundred one •
four hundred thousand, seven hundred •
twenty thousand, nine hundred •
three hundred thirty thousand, six •
five hundred three thousand, fifty •
seventy thousand, three hundred twelve •
two hundred thousand, sixty-four •
eight hundred sixty thousand •

B L A D T G W R E

• 400,700
• 503,050
• 16,701
• 20,900
• 330,006
• 200,064
• 860,000
• 70,312

What goes up but never comes down?

<u>Y</u> <u>O</u> <u>U</u> <u>R</u>   <u>A</u> <u>G</u> <u>E</u>

How Much Is a Million?

You may play this game with a partner.

1. Mark off 8 index cards or pieces of paper into 4 sections as shown.

a.	b.	
		fold
c.	d.	

fold

2. Pick a number from the list at the right. In each section of the card, write the number in one of the following ways:
   a. standard form
   b. expanded form (symbols)
   c. expanded form (words)
   d. word form

5741	1781
2346	3752
8683	7534
9266	4812

A completed card for the number 7284 looks like this:

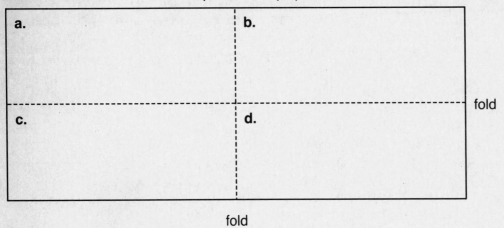

a. 7284	b. 7000 + 200 + 80 + 4
c. 7 thousands 2 hundreds 8 tens 4 ones	d. seven thousand two hundred eighty-four

3. Cut each card into 4 smaller cards to make a deck of 32 cards.

4. Play Concentration. You need two cards with the same number to make a match. At the end of play, the player who has the most cards wins.

1.11 PRACTICE

for pages 22–23

Rounding Larger Numbers

Follow the directions for each set of numbers. Circle the answer and the letter or symbol next to it.

Round to the nearest ten.

1. 25
  20 T
  (30 E)

2. 82
  (80 A)
  90 I

3. 127
  120 R
  (130 E)

4. 325
  320 G
  (330 E)

Round to the nearest hundred.

5. 390
  300 U
  (400 O)

6. 247
  (200 V)
  300 R

7. 909
  (900 P)
  1000 S

8. 550
  500 T
  (600 N)

Round to the nearest thousand.

9. 680
  (1000 N)
  600 L

10. 1502
  1000 D
  (2000 L)

11. 4281
  (4000 !)
  5000 ?

12. 9857
  9000 ←
  (10,000 →)

Below each box is an exercise number. In each box write the letter or symbol that is next to your answer for that exercise. When all the boxes are completed, you will have the answer to this riddle.

What eight-letter word has only one letter in it?

→	A	N		E	N	V	E	L	O	P	E	!
12	2	8		4	9	6	3	10	5	7	1	11

(4) **11**

1.12 PRACTICE

Comparing and Ordering

Draw a line under the greatest number in each group. Circle the word next to the number.

1. 97 Boil
    705 (Drop)
    423 Put

2. 388 (it)
    326 the
    362 in

3. 689 (four)
    652 each
    630 egg

4. 1323 times
    987 hours
    1360 (feet)

5. 715 At
    823 (For)
    563 In

6. 113 one
    103 more
    131 (the)

7. 948 than
    1065 last
    1087 (first)

8. 7582 each
    8423 (three)
    7681 both

9. 96 hours
    9610 (feet)
    960 times

10. 865 it
    856 you
    876 (the)

11. 5697 (egg)
    5690 can't
    5679 big

12. 9926 have
    9906 ever
    9932 (will)

13. 1987 always
    2000 know
    3000 (not)

14. 3921 (hit)
    2680 break
    3438 open

15. 2844 eggs
    2385 shell
    3209 (anything)

Write each word you circled in order on each of the numbered lines below. They will answer this riddle.

How can you drop an egg 3 feet without breaking it?

Drop	it	four	feet
1	2	3	4
For	the	first	three
5	6	7	8
feet	the	egg	will
9	10	11	12
not	hit	anything	
13	14	15	

1.13 PRACTICE

Identifying Money

Figure out the amount of money listed in the first two rings of each section of the money wheel. Write the amount in the third ring.

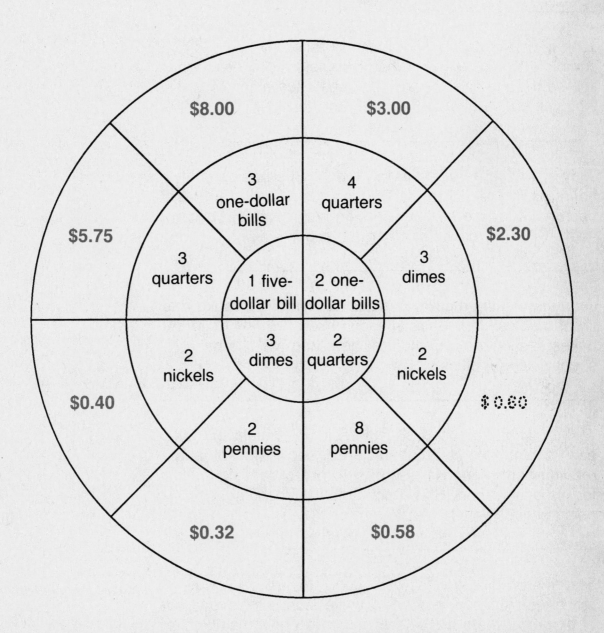

$8.00 $3.00

$5.75   3 one-dollar bills   4 quarters $2.30

3 quarters   1 five-dollar bill   2 one-dollar bills   3 dimes

2 nickels   3 dimes   2 quarters   2 nickels

$0.40 $0.60

2 pennies   8 pennies

$0.32 $0.58

Name_____ Date_____

1.14 PRACTICE

Problem Solving Strategy: **Make a Table**

Solve each problem. Make a table if it helps.

1. Chris wants to buy a dog. The dog costs $68. Chris already has $35. She can save $12 a week. How many weeks will it take Chris to save enough for the dog?

3 weeks
_____

2. John is making a model airplane. It takes 29 steps to complete the model. John has completed 12 steps. John figures that he can complete 2 steps each night. How long will it take him to complete the model?

9 nights
_____

3. Judy is writing a social studies report. She has spent 4 hours on the report so far. She intends to spend 2 hours each night for the next 5 nights on her report. How many hours will Judy spend in all on her report?

14 hours
_____

4. Jenny is making muffins. It takes 10 minutes to bake one tin of muffins. Jenny has already baked two tins. If Jenny bakes one more tin of muffins, how long will she have spent baking muffins?

30 minutes in all
_____

5. Joshua wants to spend 30 minutes doing homework for each subject. He has math, science, social studies, and reading homework. He also has 1 hour of reading to do for his book report. How much time will Joshua spend doing school work?

3 hours of school work
_____

6. Jason is building a small duck pond. He uses 12 white stones for a seat. He needs 2 white stones for every foot of border. If there are 10 feet of border, how many white stones will Jason need?

32 white stones
_____

1.15 ▸ PRACTICE

Making Change

Each receipt shows the TOTAL and the CASH paid for each purchase. Write the coins and bills you could receive as change.

Accept 2 quarters or 1 half-dollar interchangeably.
Some answers may vary.

TOTAL $4.49	TOTAL $4.78
CASH $5.00	CASH $10.00
CHANGE	CHANGE

1 penny, 2 quarters

(or 1 half-dollar)

2 pennies, 2 dimes,

1 five-dollar bill

TOTAL $0.33	TOTAL $6.79
CASH $1.00	CASH $10.00
CHANGE	CHANGE

2 pennies, 1 nickel, 1 dime,

2 quarters (or 1 half-dollar)

1 penny, 2 dimes,

3 one-dollar bills

TOTAL $1.23	TOTAL $8.68
CASH $10.00	CASH $10.00
CHANGE	CHANGE

2 pennies, 3 quarters, 3 one-dollar

bills, 1 five-dollar bill

2 pennies, 1 nickel, 1 quarter,

1 one-dollar bill

TOTAL $5.85	TOTAL $3.12
CASH $10.00	CASH $5.00
CHANGE	CHANGE

1 nickel, 1 dime,

4 one-dollar bills

3 pennies, 1 dime, 3 quarters,

1 one-dollar bill

1.16 ▸ PRACTICE   for pages 32–33

Money Sense

Exchange each amount to get as many quarters as you can. Circle the letter of the number.

1. $1.75
  W 8   (S) 7

2. $0.57
  (T) 2   B 3

3. $1.23
  S 5   (U) 4

4. 2 one-dollar bills
  (D) 8   T 12

5. $0.15
  (Y) 0   S 1

6. 16 nickels
  C 4   (N) 3

7. $5.00
  B 25   (D) 20

8. 13 dimes
  (S) 5   Z 4

9. $2.95
  (U) 11   B 13

10. two dollars and thirty cents
  M 8   (N) 9

11. $7.50
  (D) 30   E 25

12. 50 pennies
  (Y) 2   T 3

13. $3.42
  (T) 13   V 14

14. 3 one-dollar bills
  O 16   (H) 12

15. $0.98
  C 2   (R) 3

16. one dollar and eighty cents
  (S) 7   B 8

17. seven dollars and fifteen cents
  X 29   (T) 28

18. $4.25
  G 18   (R) 17

19. $8.75
  (E) 35   I 28

20. 25 nickels
  D 4   (W) 5

21. $2.01
  (K) 8   S 9

22. one dollar and thirty-seven cents
  (D) 5   F 6

Write the letters you circled to solve the riddle.

What are the two strongest days of the week?

S	A	T	U	R	D	A	Y		A	N	D		S	U	N	D	A	Y	-
1		2	3		4		5			6	7		8	9	10	11		12	

T	H	E		R	E	S	T		A	R	E		W	E	A	K		D	A	Y	S
13	14			15		16	17		18	19			20			21		22			

1.17 PRACTICE

Problem Solving: Not Enough Information

Solve each problem. If there is not enough information, tell what you need to know.

1. On vacation, Ray and his family visit a souvenir shop. Ray wants to buy a hat for $3. Will he have enough money left to buy a pen for 75¢?

   <u>Not enough information: You need to know how</u>

   <u>much money Ray has.</u>

2. An alligator pot holder is on sale for $5.00. Ray's sister has $6.00. How much can she save if she buys the pot holder on sale?

   <u>Not enough information: You need to know the</u>

   <u>regular price of the pot holder.</u>

3. Three flamingo pens cost $3.15. Ray's mother has $4.00 and several nickels. Does she have enough to buy the pens?

   <u>yes</u>

4. A T-shirt's regular price is $5.00. The sale price is $2.00 off the regular price. How much will Ray save buying the T-shirt on sale?

   <u>He will save $2.00.</u>

5. The sale price of a large T-shirt is $7.00. Ray's father has $10.00. How much can he save by buying the T-shirt on sale?

   <u>Not enough information: You need to know the</u>

   <u>cost when the T-shirt is not on sale.</u>

6. The airplane for home leaves at 12:00 noon. Ray hopes he will be home in time for his favorite television show at 8:00 P.M. Will he get there in time?

   <u>Not enough information: You need to know how</u>

   <u>long the plane trip is.</u>

2.1 ▶ PRACTICE

for pages 42–43

Properties and Rules

Write the letter of the exercise that has the same answer.

1. 99,673 + 119   _____c_____   a. 525 + 457

2. 457 − 457   _____b_____   b. 2 − 2

3. (63 + 9) + 884   _____d_____   c. 119 + 99,673

4. 2291 + 0   _____e_____   d. 63 + (9 + 884)

5. (525 + 0) + 457   _____a_____   e. 0 + 2291

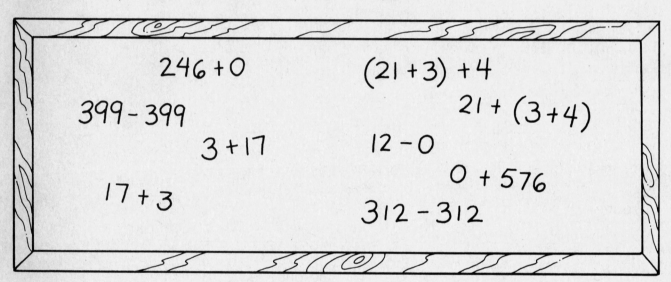

246 + 0

399 − 399

3 + 17

17 + 3

(21 + 3) + 4

21 + (3 + 4)

12 − 0

0 + 576

312 − 312

Write the answer.

6. 35 + 126 = 126 + __35__

7. 291 + 0 = __291__

8. 123 − __123__ = 0

9. 612 + 339 = __339__ + 612

10. 0 + __182__ = 182

11. 9 + (__8__ + 4) = 8 + (9 + 4)

12. 526 − __0__ = 526

13. __408__ + 222 = 222 + 408

14. __423__ − 423 = 0

15. 724 − 0 = __724__

16. 836 + __98__ = 98 + 836

17. (6 + 18) + 25 = 6 + (__18__ + 25)

18. 35 + (36 + 37) = (37 + __36__) + 35

19. (76 + 32) + 87 = (__87__ + 32) + 76

20. 55 + (99 + 88) = (55 + 88) + __99__

21. (108 + __127__) + 201 = (127 + 201) + 108

2.2 ▸ PRACTICE   for pages 44–45

Addition and Subtraction

Find the matching addition problem in the second column.
Write the letter on the line next to the first column.

_____b_____ **1.** 28 + 9   **a.** 45 + 5 + 3

_____f_____ **2.** 7 + 256   **b.** 20 + 8 + 9

_____a_____ **3.** 8 + 45   **c.** 40 + 5 + 7

_____d_____ **4.** 256 + 9   **d.** 256 + 4 + 5

_____c_____ **5.** 45 + 7   **e.** 147 + 3 + 3

_____g_____ **6.** 8 + 147   **f.** 256 + 4 + 3

_____h_____ **7.** 8 + 98   **g.** 147 + 3 + 5

_____e_____ **8.** 147 + 6   **h.** 98 + 2 + 6

56 + 9

35 + 8

157 + 8

215 + 9

Write the answer. Use mental math.

9. 18 + 8 = _26_   **10.** 66 + 7 = _73_   **11.** 39 + 4 = _43_

12. 58 + 3 = _61_   **13.** 75 + 6 = _81_   **14.** 27 + 4 = _31_

15. 81 + 9 = _90_   **16.** 44 + 8 = _52_   **17.** 78 + 7 = _85_

18. 48 − 7 = _41_   **19.** 54 − 6 = _48_   **20.** 96 − 9 = _87_

21. 37 − 8 = _29_   **22.** 65 − 7 = _58_   **23.** 24 − 5 = _19_

24. 11 − 3 = _8_   **25.** 71 − 4 = _67_   **26.** 83 − 9 = _74_

27. 74 − 7 = _67_   **28.** 42 − 6 = _36_   **29.** 16 − 8 = _8_

30. 68 − 9 = _59_   **31.** 20 − 5 = _15_   **32.** 33 − 4 = _29_

2.3 ▶ PRACTICE

Using 5, 50, and 500

Write the sum. Use mental math.

1. 35 + 15 = _____50_____
2. 35 + 45 = _____80_____
3. 75 + 35 = _____110_____
4. 350 + 150 = _____500_____
5. 85 + 65 = _____150_____
6. 625 + 255 = _____880_____
7. 600 + 350 = _____950_____
8. 805 + 105 = _____910_____
9. 7500 + 1500 = _____9000_____
10. 7050 + 1050 = _____8100_____
11. 550 + 540 = _____1090_____
12. 265 + 285 = _____550_____
13. 745 + 235 = _____980_____
14. 2705 + 2305 = _____5010_____
15. 885 + 125 = _____1010_____
16. 2235 + 6315 = _____8550_____
17. 6195 + 3315 = _____9510_____
18. 3500 + 4500 = _____8000_____
19. 5350 + 2650 = _____8000_____
20. 1205 + 7705 = _____8910_____

Circle each digit below that appears in any of the answers to exercises 1–20.

⓪ ① 2 3 4 ⑤ 6 7 ⑧ ⑨

S   N   B   G   W   T   O   L   E   I

The letters below the circled numbers, when rearranged, spell the answer to the riddle: (HINT: One of the letters is used twice.)

"In what game does love have no value?"

Answer: ___T___ ___E___ ___N___ ___N___ ___I___ ___S___

2.4 PRACTICE

Problem Solving Strategy: Make a Diagram

Solve each problem. Make a diagram when it helps.

1. Janet has a garden that measures 25 feet by 25 feet. She wants to build a fence around the garden 2 feet from the edge. How much fencing does Janet need?

   116 feet

2. She will plant tomatoes in the first 4 rows of the garden. The first row will be 1 foot from the edge of the garden. Each row will be 1 foot wide, and there will be 2 feet of space between rows. How many feet will the first 4 rows take up? **11 feet**

3. It takes Lois 1 hour to weed 1 row of her flower garden. If she starts at 9:00 A.M., when will she finish weeding 3 rows? **She will finish at 12:00 P.M.**

4. Rick's dog, Ginger, is lying next to the pool. Ginger gets up and takes 5 steps away from the pool. Then, she takes 10 more steps away. Then, she takes 10 steps back toward the pool and then 5 steps away. Finally, Ginger takes 10 steps back and lies down again. Where does she lie down?

   She lies down where she started.

5. Connie has a pool that is 20 feet square. Around the pool, she builds a fence that is 5 feet from the edge of the pool. How long is any one side of the fence?

   30 feet

6. Rick's pool is 30 feet long. Rick has picnic tables that are 8 feet long. He wants to put the tables lengthwise along one long side of the pool. If he leaves 2 feet between tables, how many tables can he fit along the pool? **3 tables**

2.5 ▶ PRACTICE

Estimating Sums

Circle pairs of numbers whose sum is about 100. Choose pairs of numbers that are next to each other vertically, horizontally or diagonally.

Answers will vary but may include those shown.

36	18	17	84	92	30	45	50	70	33
12	62	61	70	49	7	33	12	86	94
90	71	84	99	26	24	28	3	75	52
62	85	95	72	53	48	31	96	51	27
20	37	56	30	89	13	72	93	35	26

Write an estimate of each sum using front-end estimation. Then adjust and write your adjusted estimate. Answers may vary.

1.
```
    732
  + 270
```
Est. 900
Adj. 1000

2.
```
    598
  + 503
```
Est. 1000
Adj. 1100

3.
```
    540
    162
  + 204
```
Est. 800
Adj. 900

4.
```
    225
    280
    245
  + 250
```
Est. 800
Adj. 1000

5.
```
    190
    312
    253
  + 352
```
Est. 900
Adj. 1100

6.
```
   $3.70
    3.24
  + 2.03
```
Est. $8.00
Adj. $9.00

7.
```
   $2.65
    2.40
    2.10
  + 1.85
```
Est. $7.00
Adj. $9.00

8.
```
   $2.44
    1.60
    2.82
  + 2.15
```
Est. $7.00
Adj. $9.00

9.
```
   $3.42
    3.60
    2.08
  + 1.01
```
Est. $9.00
Adj. $10.00

10.
```
   $4.62
    3.40
    1.03
  + 1.95
```
Est. $9.00
Adj. $11.00

11. 244 + 160 + 382 + 215 = Est. 800   Adj. 1000

12. 84 + 219 + 342 + 360 = Est. 800   Adj. 1000

13. $1.00 + $1.18 + $3.80 + $2.22 = Est. $7.00   Adj. $8.00

2.6 PRACTICE

for pages 52–53

Adding 2- and 3-Digit Numbers

Add. Use the clues to solve the puzzle.

A 1	3	B 6	C 2	■	D 5	E 6	F 7
4	■	G 4	0	H 3	■	I 8	8
J 6	K 5	■	L 1	2	M 7	■	0
■	N 7	O 4	■	■	P 3	Q 7	■
R 1	■	S 3	T 9	U 1	■	V 4	W 1
X 8	0	■	Y 8	0	Z 2	■	8
0	■	AA 7	■	BB 1	4	CC 6	3
DD 1	2	9	8	■	EE 3	7	4

ACROSS

A. 631 + 731
D. 85 + 482
G. 375 + 28
I. 32 + 56
J. 39 + 26
L. 19 + 108
N. 37 + 37
P. 13 + 24

S. 355 + 36
V. 17 + 24
X. 32 + 48
Y. 779 + 23
BB. 789 + 674
DD. 866 + 432
EE. 344 + 30

DOWN

A. 130 + 16
B. 55 + 9
C. 99 more than 102
E. 52 + 16
F. 731 + 49
H. 25 + 7
K. 38 + 19
M. 28 + 45
O. 11 + 32

Q. 54 + 20
R. 944 + 857
T. 49 + 49
U. 63 + 38
W. 846 + 988
Z. 89 + 154
AA. 73 + 6
CC. 33 + 34

2.7 ► PRACTICE for pages 54–55

Three or More Addends

Write each sum. Use the answers and the letters to solve the riddle below.

A.	B.	C.	D.	E.
74	180	327	26	698
78	392	46	78	1824
82	647	227	87	2210
+ 56	+ 654	+ 514	34	+ 3069
290	1873	1114	+ 43	7801
			268	

F.	G.	L.	M.	N.
$23.50	2480	1695	88	$40.79
12.00	862	1050	62	1.39
2.50	1595	1289	47	2.53
+ .79	+ 1184	+ 7498	36	+ .50
$38.79	6121	11,532	+ 55	$45.21
			288	

O. $4.89 + $21.71 + $6.25 + $1.04 = _____$33.89_____

P. $69.71 + $0.89 + $4.07 + $7.75 = _____$82.42_____

R. 407 + 246 + 38 + 5287 = _____5978_____

S. 2381 + 1642 + 498 + 1175 = _____5696_____

What do you get from confused chickens?

S	C	R	A	M	B	L	E	D
5696	1114	5978	290	288	1873	11,532	7801	268

E	G	G	S
7801	6121	6121	5696

2.8 ▸ PRACTICE   for page 56

Estimating Sums by Rounding

Estimate the sum by rounding to the greatest value. Find the estimated sum in the Answer Box. Write the estimated sum on the line and the code letter in the small box. You will not use every sum. You will use some sums more than once.

Answer Box

70 L	80 H	90 U	100 T	110 A	150 Y	160 P	400 D	500 S	600 O	700 B
800 M	900 R	1300 I								

1. 612 + 739 = _1300_ [:]

2. 108 + 134 + 427 = _600_ [O]

3. 197 + 159 = _400_ [D]

4. 64 + 43 = _100_ [T]

5.   74
    + 42
    ‾‾‾‾‾
    _110_ [A]

6.   21
    + 47
    ‾‾‾‾‾
    _70_ [L]

7.   444
    + 485
    ‾‾‾‾‾
    _900_ [R]

8. 27 + 68 = _100_ [T]

9. 381 + 878 = _1300_ [I]

10. 51 + 36 = _90_ [U]

11. 26 + 14 + 43 = _80_ [H]

12.   223
    + 662
    ‾‾‾‾‾
    _900_ [R]

13.   85
    + 72
    ‾‾‾‾‾
    _160_ [P]

14.   581
    + 205
    ‾‾‾‾‾
    _800_ [M]

To answer the riddle, write each estimated sum's code letter on the line above the number of the exercise. Some letters are already in the riddle.

What is one way to double your money?

H	O	L	D	:	T	U	P
11.	6.	3.	1.	8.	10.	13.

T	O	A	M	I	R	R	O	R
4.	5.	14.	9.	12.	2.	7.

2.9 ▶ PRACTICE

Estimating Differences

Estimate each difference to the greatest place.

Answers may vary. Accept any estimate in the range given.

1.	92	2.	78	3.	89	4.	378
	− 14		− 44		− 31		− 103
	70–80		30–40		50–60		200–300

5.	603	6.	922	7.	4864	8.	3765
	− 485		− 196		− 2106		− 3241
	100–200		700–800		2000–3000		500–1000

9.	78,236	10.	9872	11.	56,012	12.	5782
	− 41,921		− 5186		− 39,285		− 5316
	30,000–40,000		4000–5000		20,000–30,000		400–1000

13. 543 − 182 = ___300–400___ 14. 427 − 262 = ___100–200___

15. 779 − 201 = ___500–600___ 16. 973 − 448 = ___500–600___

17. 9487 − 3692 = ___5000–6000___ 18. 726 − 703 = ___0–30___

19. 6397 − 2707 = ___3000–4000___ 20. 4462 − 1778 = ___2000–3000___

21. 7640 − 2126 = ___5000–6000___ 22. 9864 − 2371 = ___7000–8000___

23.	4382	24.	9761	25.	677	26.	8547
	− 3729		− 2163		− 213		− 6371
	0–1000		7000–8000		400–500		2000–3000

27.	793	28.	6287	29.	5318	30.	944
	− 241		− 1763		− 3891		− 396
	500–600		4000–5000		1000–2000		500–600

31.	78,845	32.	793	33.	5790	34.	799
	− 21,341		− 538		− 2339		− 667
	50,000–60,000		200–300		3000–4000		100–200

2.10 PRACTICE

for pages 60–61

Subtracting Greater Numbers

Write the difference. Then match the letter with the answer below to solve the riddle.

A. 131
   − 124
   7

B. 2523
   − 196
   2327

C. 946
   − 832
   114

D. 95
   − 77
   18

E. $10.27
   − $ 5.83
   $4.44

F. 863
   − 485
   378

G. 1886
   − 1753
   133

H. 933
   − 846
   87

I. 54
   − 45
   9

J. 382 ft
   − 168 ft
   214 ft

K. 450
   − 365
   85

L. 4776
   − 2775
   2001

M. 572
   − 466
   106

N. 82
   − 58
   24

O. 411 ft
   − 187 ft
   224 ft

P. 100 mi − 65 mi = ____**35 mi**____

Q. 100 mi − 83 mi = ____**17 mi**____

R. 2462 m − 2393 m = ____**69 m**____

S. 242 m − 163 m = ____**79 m**____

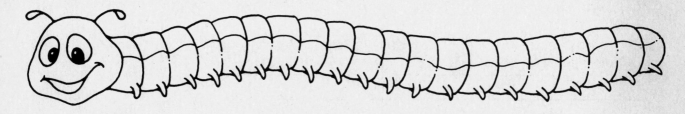

What did the centipede say to its mother?

L	O	O	K,	M	A,	N	O
2001	224 ft	224 ft	85	106	7	24	224 ft

H	A	N	D	S!
87	7	24	18	79 m

2.11 ▷ PRACTICE
for pages 62–63

Problem Solving: Using Math Sense

Read each story. Does the underlined sentence make sense?
Tell why or why not. Answers may vary; possible responses are given.

1. The number 4 key is broken on Jason's calculator. He wants to find 351 − 34. "I know," said Jason. "I will subtract 33 and then subtract 1."

Yes, subtracting 33 and then 1 more is the same

as subtracting 34.

2. Donald, Monica, and Ramon are sharing a pizza. The pie is cut into 8 slices. "Let's share the pie equally," Donald says. "We will each eat 2 slices. Then I will cut the remaining slices in half so that we can split them evenly."

No, the 4 half-slices cannot be split evenly

among 3 people.

3. The drive from Greentown to Far Hills takes $4\frac{1}{2}$ hours. The Stein family wants to arrive in Far Hills by 4:00 P.M. Mr. Stein says, "We had better leave Greentown no later than 11:30 in the morning."

Yes, there are $4\frac{1}{2}$ hours between 11:30 A.M. and

4:00 P.M.

4. Jane is 5 years old. Her sister Kate is twice as old. Five years from now, Kate will still be twice as old as Jane.

No, five years from now Jane will be 10 years old

and her sister Kate will be 15 years old.

5. Tanya wants to know how much her dog weighs. She steps on the scale and sees that her own weight is 75 pounds. She steps on the scale again, holding her dog. The scale now reads 100 pounds. Tanya says, "My dog weighs 25 pounds."

Yes, the weight of the dog is the difference

between 100 pounds and 75 pounds.

2.12 PRACTICE

Zeros in Subtraction

The first place winner in the school candle sale sold 702 candles. The second place winner sold 623 candles. How many more candles did the first place winner sell than the second place winner?

You can subtract 623 from 702.

● Enough ones?
  No; regroup.
  No tens; regroup hundreds.

6 10
7̶0̶2̶
−623

● Regroup tens.

9
6 1̶0̶ 12
7̶0̶2̶
−623

● Subtract.

9
6 1̶0̶ 12
7̶0̶2̶
−623
  79

The first place winner sold 79 more candles.

Write the difference.

1.	508	2.	803	3.	940	4.	$8.09
	−472		−172		−879		− 2.22
	36		631		61		$5.87

5.	1702	6.	2903	7.	800	8.	6001
	− 371		−1591		−359		−5873
	1331		1312		441		128

9.	2220	10.	4067	11.	2908	12.	5190
	−1782		−1970		− 732		− 163
	438		2097		2176		5027

13.	1000	14.	$100.92	15.	8040	16.	20,706
	− 973		− 63.75		−2363		−10,032
	27		$37.17		5677		10,674

2.13 PRACTICE

for pages 66–67

Using Addition and Subtraction

Solve each problem.

1. Last year, the Marvel Bakery sold 6487 apple pies, 2105 pumpkin pies, and 1876 cherry pies.

   a. How many pies did it sell altogether? _____ **10,468 pies** _____
   b. How many fewer cherry pies than pumpkin pies did it

   sell? _____ **229 fewer cherry pies** _____
   c. How many more apple pies than pumpkin and cherry

   pies together did it sell? _____ **2506 more apple pies** _____

2. The bakery sells carrot cakes for $8.75 each, banana cakes for $6.50 each, and spice cakes for $4.95 each.
   a. How much less does a spice cake cost than a carrot

   cake? _____ **$3.80** _____
   b. Mr. Phillips buys a carrot cake and a banana cake. He gives the clerk $20. How much change does he

   get? _____ **$4.75** _____

3. The bakery makes whole wheat bread and white bread. So far this year, it has made 6240 loaves of whole wheat bread and 9180 loaves of white bread.
   a. How many loaves of bread has it made so far this

   year? _____ **15,420 loaves** _____
   b. How many more loaves of white bread than whole

   wheat bread has it made? _____ **2940 loaves of white bread** _____
   c. The bakery wants to make a total of 30,000 loaves of bread this year. How many more loaves must it make

   to reach this goal? _____ **14,580 more loaves** _____

4. The bakery used 1127 eggs in May, 942 eggs in June, and 1488 eggs in July.

   a. How many eggs did it use in all three months? _____ **3557 eggs** _____
   b. How many fewer eggs did it use in July than in May

   and June together? _____ **581 fewer eggs** _____

2.14 ▸ PRACTICE

Problem Solving: Using Strategies

The Hanson family is spending a week at a resort. Use the map to solve each problem.

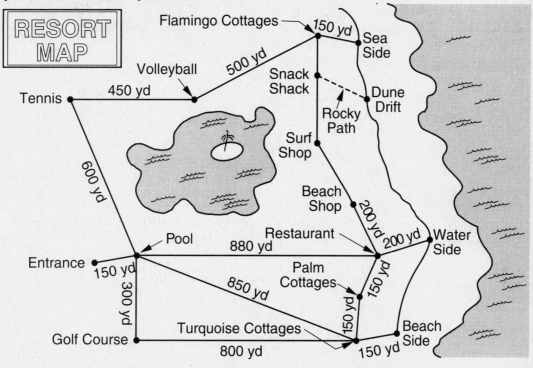

1. The Hanson family's cottage is 1030 yards from the pool.

Where is the Hansons' cottage? _____**Palm Cottages**_____

2. Mr. and Mrs. Hanson are at the restaurant, and they want to go to the golf course. What is the shortest route?

How long is it? _____**restaurant–Palm Cottages–Turquoise Cottages–golf;**_____

1100 yards

3. Which of the following is a good estimate of the length of the rocky path?
   a. 50 yards   **b.** 200 yards   **c.** 500 yards

200 yards

4. Jamie is on the beach at Dune Drift. About how long is the shortest route to the volleyball court?

Answers may vary: There are two routes that are both about 900 yards.

_____

Name_____ Date_____

3.1 PRACTICE

Collecting and Recording Data

Use the facts in this printout to complete each table. Decide which facts belong in each table. (Some facts may not belong in either table.) Cross out each fact after you write it in a table.

In the 1984 Summer and Winter Olympics, Italy won 34 medals and Romania won 53. A football team has 11 players. Canada won 48 Summer and Winter Olympic medals in 1984. A basketball team has 5 players. A swan's wing span can be 8 feet long. A baseball team has 9 players. Norway won 12 Summer and Winter Olympic medals in 1984. A volleyball team has 6 players; an ice hockey team has 6. A condor's wing span can be 9 feet long. In the 1984 Summer and Winter Olympics, Finland won 26 medals.

1.

Olympic Medals Won in 1984

Country	Number of Medals
Italy	34
Romania	53
Canada	48
Norway	12
Finland	26

2.

Required Number of Players in Different Sports

Sport	Number of Players
football	11
basketball	5
baseball	9
volleyball	6
ice hockey	6

3. In what order did you list the data in the second table above? How else can you order the data in the table? **Answers may vary but may include: follow the order of the printout; listed alphabetically by sport; listed by number of players – greatest to least or least to greatest.**

4. Make up a title for a table in which you could put the facts that you did not cross out on the printout. **Answers may vary but may include: Birds' Wing Span**

3.2 ▼PRACTICE

Organizing Data in a Bar Graph

Complete the table and the bar graph. Use the data in the table to complete the bar graph. Then use the bar graph to answer each question.

Circus Job Choices of Fourth-Graders at Carver School		
Job Choice	Tally	Total
Bareback Rider |卌 |||	8
Clown	卌 卌 卌		16
Lion Tamer	卌 卌 卌 |||	18
Trapeze Artist	卌 卌 ||	12

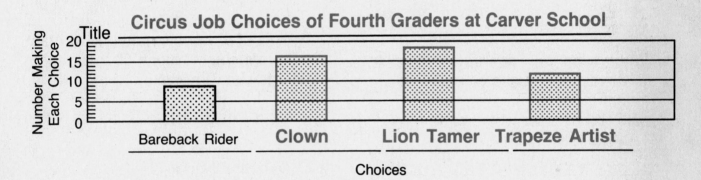

Circus Job Choices of Fourth Graders at Carver School

Number Making Each Choice

Choices: Bareback Rider, Clown, Lion Tamer, Trapeze Artist

1. How did the table help you to choose a title for the bar graph?

I used the title of the table as the title of the bar graph.

2. Suppose you decide to organize the bar graph from the most popular job choice to the least popular. Which job choice would you show first? Which job choice would you show last? **You would show the lion tamer first and the bareback rider last.**

3. Suppose you added a bar to show that 23 people want to be acrobats. What would the top number on the number line of the graph be? **25**

3.3 ▶ PRACTICE

Problem Solving Strategy: Make a List

Solve each problem. Make a list when it helps.

1. Calvin's family is driving from White Bluff to Hillsdale. What different routes of less than 175 miles can they take?

   White Bluff–Gallatin–Hillsdale,

   White Bluff–Gallatin–Holtville–

   Hillsdale, White Bluff–Fayette–

   Cobb City–Hillsdale, White

   Bluff–Fayette–Santa Luna–Cobb

   City–Hillsdale, White Bluff–

   Santa Luna–Cobb City–Hillsdale

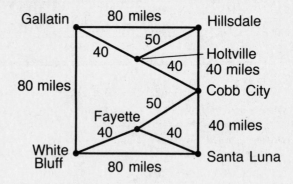

2. Lorna sees the word *feats* in a book. She notices that she can use the letters in *feats* to make the word *safe*. What other words can be made with the letters in *feats*?

   Answers may vary but may

   include: eat, east, eats, fat, sat,

   fast, aft, seat, tea, teas, set, fate

4. Alice, Barbara, and Christine are triplets. On their birthday, their parents sing "Happy Birthday" 3 times, once for each of them. In how many different orders can their parents sing the song to them?

   6 orders

3. Tim goes away for the weekend and takes 3 pairs of shorts and 3 shirts. He has one red, one yellow, and one blue pair of shorts and one red, one yellow and one blue shirt. How many different combinations of shirts and shorts can Tim make?

   9 different combinations

5. Tami is making a secret code. She assigns a series of three shapes to each letter of the alphabet. For example, for the letter *A* she uses ○△□, for *B* △△□, for *C* □○△. Using only 3 shapes, can she make a different combination for each letter of the alphabet?

   yes

3.4 PRACTICE for pages 82–83

Pictographs

Use the pictograph to answer each question below.

Number of Valentines Made by Students in Miss Frank's Class

Anna	♡ ♡ ♡ ♡ ♡
Trisha	♡ ◗
Paco	♡ ♡ ♡ ♡ ◗
Yolanda	♡ ♡ ♡
Barry	♡ ♡ ♡ ◗
Paul	♡ ♡ ◗
Rachel	♡ ♡ ♡

♡ = 10 valentines   ◗ = 5 valentines

1. Who made the most valentines? How many valentines did that person make?
   __**Anna; 50 valentines**__

2. Paul wants to make 10 more valentines for his family. If he does that, how many
   valentines will he have made in all? ____**35 valentines**_____

3. How many more valentines must Trisha make to have the same number of
   valentines as Rachel? ____**15 more valentines**_____

4. Anna made a valentine collage for her mother. She used 15 of her valentines in
   the collage. How many valentines does she have left to send to friends?
   35 valentines

5. Rachel gets a valentine from a classmate. The valentine is signed "Guess Who?"
   The sender wrote, "This is my 30th and last valentine." Who sent Rachel the
   mystery valentine? ____**Yolanda**_____

6. Someone else in the class made 30 valentines. Why do you think that person did
   not send the mystery valentine? ____**Rachel would not have sent herself a**____
   ____**valentine.**_____

3.5 ▸ PRACTICE

Line Graphs

Greg Taft's company, Butterfly Toys, sells handmade toys.
Use the line graph to answer each question about his company's sales.

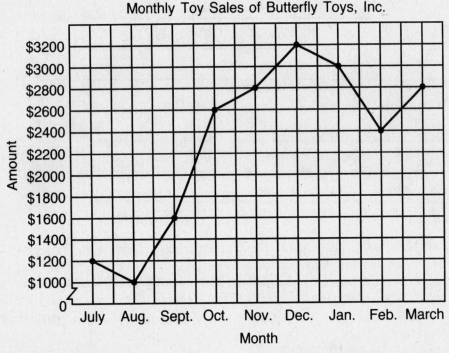

Monthly Toy Sales of Butterfly Toys, Inc.

1. Between which two months did sales increase the most?

September and October

2. Between which two months did sales increase by only $200?

October and November

3. In which month did Butterfly Toys sell the most toys?

December

4. By how much did sales go down between December and February?

$800

5. In which two months were sales the same?

November and March

6. What is the difference in sales between the lowest point and the highest point on the graph?

$2200

7. Greg believes that his company needs to sell more than $1500 worth of toys a month to be successful. What was the first month that happened?

September

8. In March, the Toys by Mail Company had sales of $2500. Which company had higher sales that month, Toys by Mail or Butterfly Toys? How much higher were the sales?

Butterfly Toys; $300 higher

3.6 ▸PRACTICE   for pages 86–87

Circle Graphs

Use the clues to fill in the circle graph.

- The City Book Club raised $560 to buy books for the school library. The greatest amount of money came from a walk-a-thon.
- A crafts fair and a bake sale raised equal amounts of money.
- The amount received from club dues was twice as much as the amount raised from the bake sale.

Money Raised by the City Book Club for School Library

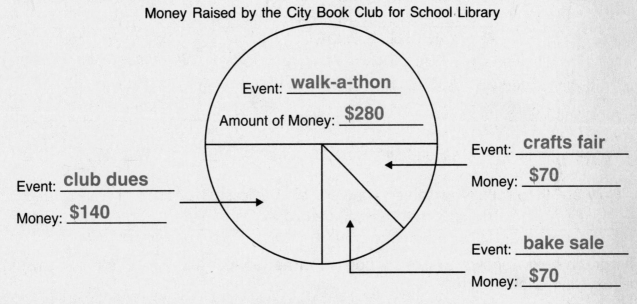

Event: **walk-a-thon**
Amount of Money: **$280**

Event: **crafts fair**
Money: **$70**

Event: **club dues**
Money: **$140**

Event: **bake sale**
Money: **$70**

Use the graph to answer each question.

1. What fraction of the money was raised by the walk-a-thon?
   $\frac{1}{2}$ **of the money**

2. What fraction of the money came from club dues?
   $\frac{1}{4}$ **of the money**

3. How much more money would the club have had to receive from the bake sale to match the amount raised by the walk-a-thon? **$210 more**

4. The Book Club wants to raise $600 for the school library. According to the circle graph, how much more do club members need to raise? **$40 more**

5. A company promised to match the total amount that the book club received from both the crafts fair and the bake sale. How much money must the company give? **$140**

3.7 PRACTICE   for pages 88–89

Using Data

Five students in Ms. Curran's class save newspapers and cans for recycling.
Use the bar graphs below to answer each question.

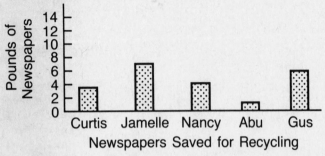
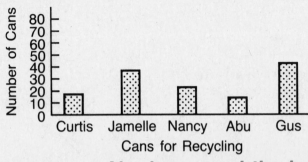

Newspapers Saved for Recycling

Cans for Recycling

1. Who has saved the least quantity of newspapers for recycling? Who has saved the most? _____ **Abu has saved the least and Jamelle has saved the most**

2. Which students have saved fewer than 30 cans? _____ **Curtis, Nancy, and Abu**

3. How are the graphs the same? How are they different? _____ **Answers may include:**
   The students are the same. Intervals and subjects are different.

The graph below shows how many pounds of newspaper Ms. Curran's class saved for recycling each month.

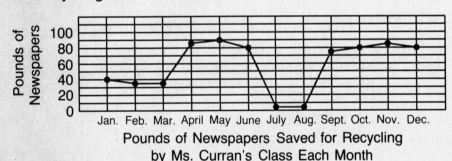

Pounds of Newspapers Saved for Recycling
by Ms. Curran's Class Each Month

Use the graph to answer each question.

4. Only 10 students in Ms. Curran's class were involved when recycling began in January. Another 15 students became involved later in the year. In which month do you think the other students became involved? Explain.
   April; the quantity of newspapers saved increased noticeably

5. In which months were the smallest quantities of newspapers saved for recycling? Why do you think that is so?
   July and August; school is closed during those months.

(4) **38**

3.8 PRACTICE

Problem Solving: Does the Answer Fit the Problem?

Circle the letter of the answer to the question.

1. Donna wants to buy 2 bags of dog food and 1 package of dog treats. Each bag of food costs $3.98, and the dog treats cost $2.49. Is $10 enough to buy those items?
   a. The items cost $10.45.
   b. Yes, $10 is enough.
   c. No, $10 is not enough.
   d. She needs 45¢ more.

2. Richard bought a puppy in 1987. His parents bought a puppy in 1989. Which dog is older?
   a. His parents' dog is younger.
   b. Richard's dog is 4 years old.
   c. His parents' dog is 2 years old.
   d. Richard's dog is older.

3. Tom bought a 15-foot length of leather to make 2 leashes. He needs 7 feet of leather for each leash. How much leather will be left?
   a. Tom will use 14 feet of leather.
   b. There will be 1 foot of leather left.
   c. Tom has enough for 2 leashes.
   d. There is not enough left over for another leash.

4. Erica buys a bag of cat food. She feeds her cat 1 cup every day. There are 12 cups of cat food in the bag. Is there enough to feed her cat for 2 weeks?
   a. No, there is not enough.
   b. The food will feed the cat for 12 days.
   c. Erica will need 2 cups of food.
   d. The cat will be hungry for 2 days.

5. Kim's parrot says 5 words. Kim teaches the parrot 1 word a week. How many words will the parrot be able to say after 3 weeks?
   a. The parrot can make up 3 sentences.
   b. Kim will spend 3 weeks teaching the parrot.
   c. The parrot will be able to say 8 words.
   d. The parrot will be able to say 3 new words.

6. Franklin has $20. He buys a bird cage for $9.98, a parakeet for $4.98, and bird seed for $2.59. He wants to buy bird treats for $1.98. Can he do that and have enough to take the bus home? The bus costs $1.
   a. He will have 47¢ left.
   b. He will need 53¢ more to take the bus.
   c. He cannot buy bird treats.
   d. He does not have enough for the bus.

3.9 PRACTICE/RECORDING SHEET for pages 92–93

Making Predictions

Answers may vary.

	Tally	Total
Blue		
Red		
Green		
Yellow		

	Tally	Total
Blue		
Red		
Green		
Yellow		

	Tally	Total
Blue		
Red		
Green		
Yellow		

	Tally	Total
Blue		
Red		
Green		
Yellow		

Marble Pick Bar Graph

Number of Throws — Red, Blue, Green, Yellow

3.10 ▸ **PRACTICE** for pages 94–95

Comparing Probabilities

At the fair there is a booth called Wheels of Wonder. Before fairgoers spin a wheel, they try to guess where it will stop. If they guess right, they win a prize.

1.

Write which wheel you would choose and why.

1. You want the wheel to stop on a diamond.
   Wheel 1, it has the largest space for a diamond.

2.

2. You do not want the wheel to stop on a square.
   Wheel 4, it has the smallest space for a square.

3. You want the wheel to stop on a star.
   Wheel 2, it has the largest space for a star.

3.

4. You do not want the wheel to stop on a heart.
   Wheel 2, it has no space for a heart.

4.

Write what the chances are of the result occurring.

5. Wheel 2 stops on a star. __3__ out of __5__ .

6. Wheel 3 stops on a heart. __1__ out of __6__ .

7. Wheel 4 stops on a star. __1__ out of __8__ .

Which result is more likely to happen? Write *a*, *b*, or *same*.

8. a. Wheel 3 stops on a star. **b.** Wheel 1 stops on a diamond. __b__

9. a. Wheel 2 stops on a star. **b.** Wheel 3 stops on a square. __a__

10. a. Wheel 4 stops on a heart. **b.** Wheel 1 stops on a diamond. __same__

11. a. Wheel 3 stops on a star. **b.** Wheel 1 stops on a star. __same__

12. a. Wheel 3 stops on a square. **b.** Wheel 3 stops on a diamond. __same__

13. a. Wheel 2 stops on a star. **b.** Wheel 2 stops on a square. __a__

Name_____ Date_____

3.11 PRACTICE/RECORDING SHEET for pages 96–97

Listing What Can Happen

2 4 8		5 9 3 6
248		5369
284	Answers will vary.	5396
824		5639
842		5693
428		5936
482		5963
		9635
		9653
		9536
		9563
		9356
		9365
		3659
		3695
		3965
		3956
		3569
		3596
		6359
		6395
		6539
		6593
		6935
		6953

3.12 ▸ PRACTICE/RECORDING SHEET for pages 98–99

Making Better Predictions

Answers will vary.

Order	Tally	Total

Answers will vary.

Order	Group A	Group B	Group C	Group D	Group E	Total

3.13 ► PRACTICE for page 100

Mental Math: Addition and Subtraction

To help you find the answer using mental math, you can do
the two operations in parentheses.
Write the answer on the line.

1. 43 + 19 (43 + 20; − 1) ___62___ (43 + 20 = 63; and 63 − 1 = 62)

2. 37 − 19 (37 − 20; + 1) ___18___ **3.** 52 + 19 (52 + 20; − 1) ___71___

4. 56 + 29 (56 + 30; − 1) ___85___ **5.** 64 − 49 (64 − 50; + 1) ___15___

6. 71 + 19 (71 + 20; − 1) ___90___ **7.** 30 − 19 (30 − 20; + 1) ___11___

8. 62 − 49 (62 − 50; + 1) ___13___ **9.** 31 + 49 (31 + 50; − 1) ___80___

10. 73 − 19 (73 − 20; + 1) ___54___ **11.** 57 − 29 (57 − 30; + 1) ___28___

12. 61 + 19 (61 + 20; − 1) ___80___ **13.** 93 − 49 (93 − 50; + 1) ___44___

14. 48 − 29 (48 − 30; + 1) ___19___ **15.** 46 + 19 (46 + 20; − 1) ___65___

16. 34 + 19 (34 + 20; − 1) ___53___ **17.** 76 − 49 (76 − 50; + 1) ___27___

18. 45 + 49 (45 + 50; − 1) ___94___ **19.** 34 + 29 (34 + 30; − 1) ___63___

20. 36 − 29 (36 − 30; + 1) ___7___ **21.** 81 − 29 (81 − 30; + 1) ___52___

22. 82 − 49 (82 − 50; + 1) ___33___ **23.** 63 − 19 (63 − 20; + 1) ___44___

24. 55 + 19 (55 + 20; − 1) ___74___ **25.** 74 + 19 (74 + 20; − 1) ___93___

26. 77 − 29 (77 − 30; + 1) ___48___ **27.** 30 − 29 (30 − 30; + 1) ___1___

Name_____ Date_____

4.1 ▸ PRACTICE

for pages 108–109

Understanding Multiplication

For each array, circle the addition sentence and the multiplication sentence that matches it. Write the letter of your answer on the numbered line at the bottom of the page.

The letters will spell out the answer to this riddle:

Why is the letter *B* like fire?

	Array	Addition Sentence	Multiplication Sentence
1.	x x x x x x x x x	(3 + 3 + 3 = 9) I 2 + 2 + 2 = 6 A	2 × 3 = 6 M (3 × 3 = 9) T
2.	x x x x	1 + 1 + 1 = 3 R (2 + 2 = 4) M	3 × 1 = 3 E (2 × 2 = 4) A
3.	x x x x x x x x x x x x	3 + 3 + 3 = 9 S (4 + 4 + 4 = 12) K	(3 × 4 = 12) E 3 × 3 = 9 I
4.	x x x x x x x x x x x x x x x x x x x x x x x x x x x x x x x x	(8 + 8 + 8 + 8 = 32) S 7 + 7 + 7 + 7 = 28 R	(4 × 8 = 32) O 4 × 7 = 28 A
5.	x x x x x x x x x x x x x x x x x x x x x x x x x x x	(9 + 9 + 9 = 27) I 8 + 8 + 8 = 24 G	8 × 3 = 24 P (9 × 3 = 27) L
6.	x x x x x x x x x x x x x x x x x x x x x	6 + 6 + 6 = 18 T (7 + 7 + 7 = 21) B	3 × 6 = 18 A (3 × 7 = 21) O
7.	x x x x x x x x x x x x	6 + 6 + 6 = 18 R (6 + 6 = 12) I	(6 × 2 = 12) L 6 × 3 = 18 N

I T   M A K E S   O I L   B O I L .
1 1   2 2 3 3 4   4 5 5   6 6 7 7

© D.C. Heath and Company

(4) **45**

4.2 ▶ PRACTICE

Multiplying by 5 and 10

Multiply to complete. Write the product.

1.

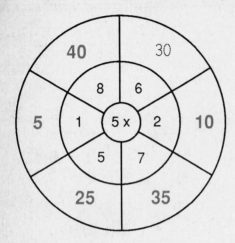

2.

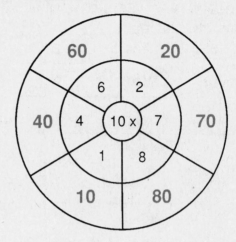

3.

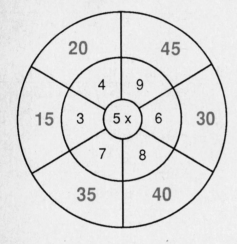

4.

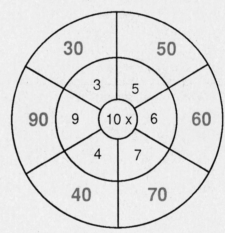

Write the product.

5.	**6.**	**7.**	**8.**	**9.**	**10.**	**11.**
8	6	7	3	8	9	5
× 5	× 10	× 5	× 5	× 10	× 5	× 10
40	60	35	15	80	45	50

12. 9 × 10 = __90__   **13.** 5 × 6 = __30__   **14.** 4 × 5 = __20__   **15.** 10 × 4 = __40__

16. 2 × 10 = __20__   **17.** 5 × 2 = __10__   **18.** 10 × 7 = __70__   **19.** 5 × 7 = __35__

Understanding Division

Write the quotient. Color each space in which the quotient is 5 or less.

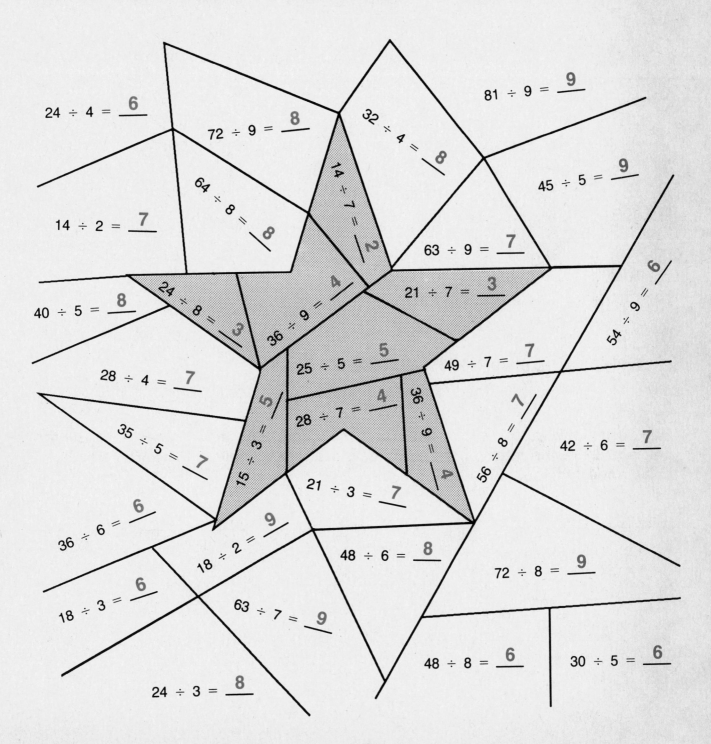

$24 \div 4 = 6$

$72 \div 9 = 8$

$32 \div 4 = 8$

$81 \div 9 = 9$

$64 \div 8 = 8$

$14 \div 7 = 2$

$45 \div 5 = 9$

$14 \div 2 = 7$

$63 \div 9 = 7$

$24 \div 8 = 3$

$36 \div 9 = 4$

$21 \div 7 = 3$

$40 \div 5 = 8$

$54 \div 9 = 6$

$25 \div 5 = 5$

$49 \div 7 = 7$

$28 \div 4 = 7$

$15 \div 3 = 5$

$28 \div 7 = 4$

$36 \div 9 = 4$

$56 \div 8 = 7$

$42 \div 6 = 7$

$35 \div 5 = 7$

$21 \div 3 = 7$

$36 \div 6 = 6$

$18 \div 2 = 9$

$48 \div 6 = 8$

$72 \div 8 = 9$

$18 \div 3 = 6$

$63 \div 7 = 9$

$48 \div 8 = 6$

$30 \div 5 = 6$

$24 \div 3 = 8$

4.4 ▸PRACTICE

Dividing by 5 and 10

Write the quotient.

T $5\overline{)5}$ → 1

A $5\overline{)25}$ → 5

K $5\overline{)40}$ → 8

O $5\overline{)15}$ → 3

F $10\overline{)90}$ → 9

R $10\overline{)70}$ → 7

E $10\overline{)20}$ → 2

H $10\overline{)60}$ → 6

F $5\overline{)45}$ → 9

R $5\overline{)35}$ → 7

C $5\overline{)20}$ → 4

E $5\overline{)10}$ → 2

E $10\overline{)20}$ → 2

A $10\overline{)50}$ → 5

O $10\overline{)30}$ → 3

K $10\overline{)80}$ → 8

H 30 ÷ 5 = __6__

F 45 ÷ 5 = __9__

C 20 ÷ 5 = __4__

T 40 ÷ 40 = __1__

R 70 ÷ 10 = __7__

F 90 ÷ 10 = __9__

Use your answers to find an important message. Find each quotient below the line and write the letter of the exercise on the line above it. The first one has been done for you.

T / A / K / E   C / A / R / E
1   5   8   2   4   5   7   2

O / F   T / H / E
3   9   1   6   2

E / A / R / T / H .
2   5   7   1   6

4.5 ▶ PRACTICE

for pages 116–117

Properties and Rules

Fill in each blank.

Row 1:   **1.** 19 × 43 = __43__ × 19 (W)   **2.** 21 × __0__ = 0 M

Row 2:   **3.** __0__ × 38 = 0 A   **4.** 36 × 1 = __36__ (I)

Row 3:   **5.** 0 ÷ 32 = __0__ (S)   **6.** __97__ ÷ 1 = 97 C

Row 4:   **7.** (45 × 3) × 16 = 45 × (3 × __16__) (C)   **8.** __57__ × 1 = 57 D

Row 5:   **9.** 82 ÷ __1__ = 82 N   **10.** 569 ÷ __569__ = 1 (O)

Row 6:   **11.** 153 × 28 = 28 × __153__ M   **12.** 34 × __1__ = 34 (N)

Row 7:   **13.** (5 × __6__) × 9 = 5 × (6 × 9) R   **14.** 29 × 0 = __0__ (S)

Row 8:   **15.** 73 ÷ __1__ = 73 (I)   **16.** 326 ÷ __326__ = 1 E

Row 9:   **17.** __47__ × 31 = 31 × 47 (N)   **18.** 29 × 0 = __0__ S

Look at each row. Decide which exercise in that row shows the property or rule listed below. Circle the letter of the exercise, and use it to solve the question below.

Row 1:   Order Property
Row 2:   Property of One
Row 3:   If you divide zero by any other number, the quotient is always zero.
Row 4:   Grouping Property
Row 5:   If you divide a number by itself, the quotient is 1.
Row 6:   Property of One
Row 7:   Property of Zero
Row 8:   If you divide a number by 1, the quotient is always that number.
Row 9:   Order Property

Answer the following question using the letters you circled.

Of which state in the United States is Madison the capital?

__W__ __I__ __S__ __C__ __O__ __N__ __S__ __I__ __N__

4.6 ▸ PRACTICE/RECORDING SHEET for pages 118–119

Making a Facts Table

	1	2	3	4	5	6	7	8	9	10
1	1	2	3	4	5	6	7	8	9	10
2	2	4	6	8	10	12	14	16	18	20
3	3	6	9	12	15	18	21	24	27	30
4	4	8	12	16	20	24	28	32	36	40
5	5	10	15	20	25	30	35	40	45	50
6	6	12	18	24	30	36	42	48	54	60
7	7	14	21	28	35	42	49	56	63	70
8	8	16	24	32	40	48	56	64	72	80
9	9	18	27	36	45	54	63	72	81	90
10	10	20	30	40	50	60	70	80	90	100

4.7 ▶ PRACTICE   for page 120

···

Choose a Computation Method: Mental Math or Paper and Pencil

The Pounders are playing the Bruisers. Use mental math or pencil and paper to solve. Below the exercise, circle which method you used. Whichever team's row has more circles wins the round. The team that wins more rounds wins the match. **Solution methods may vary.**

m m—mental math   p and p—pencil and paper

Round 1

1.	2.	3.	4.	5.
8 × 5 **40**	32 − 10 **22**	200 + 100 **300**	82 − 36 **46**	$5.23 + $3.86 **$9.09**

Pounders: p and p   p and p   m m   p and p   m m
Bruisers: m m   m m   p and p   m m   p and p

Round 2

6.	7.	8.	9.	10.
12 + 12 **24**	593 − 468 **125**	7 × 2 **14**	237 + 125 **362**	362 146 + 31 **539**

Pounders: m m   p and p   m m   p and p   p and p
Bruisers: p and p   m m   p and p m m   m m

Round 3

11.	12.	13.	14.	15.
$4.00 − $1.00 **$3.00**	$8.63 + $3.57 **$12.20**	76 − 49 **27**	10 × 4 **40**	3729 × 1 **3729**

Pounders: p and p   m m   p and p   m m   m m
Bruisers: m m   p and p   m m   p and p   p and p

Round 4

16.	17.	18.	19.	20.
293 × 0 **0**	593 471 + 56 **1120**	567 − 124 **443**	80 + 7 **87**	4 × 4 **16**

Pounders: . m m   p and p   m m   m m   p and p
Bruisers: p and p   m m   p and p   p and p   m m

(4) **51**

4.8 PRACTICE

for pages 122–123

Multiplying by 2, 4, and 8

Write <, >, or =. Circle the letter in the column of the symbol that you wrote.

	<	>	=
1. $8 \times 4 \; > \; 6 \times 2$	A	(C)	G
2. $2 \times 3 \; < \; 2 \times 6$	(a)	j	h
3. $6 \times 4 \; = \; 3 \times 8$	b	e	(l)
4. $3 \times 4 \; < \; 5 \times 8$	(v)	s	d
5. $7 \times 2 \; < \; 7 \times 8$	(i)	f	p
6. $2 \times 10 \; > \; 2 \times 5$	c	(n)	l
7. $8 \times 9 \; > \; 4 \times 7$	H	(C)	P
8. $4 \times 4 \; < \; 8 \times 10$	(o)	c	t
9. $4 \times 5 \; = \; 2 \times 10$	u	k	(o)
10. $8 \times 8 \; > \; 4 \times 8$	m	(l)	r
11. $9 \times 4 \; > \; 8 \times 3$	s	(i)	e
12. $2 \times 8 \; = \; 4 \times 4$	u	p	(d)
13. $10 \times 4 \; < \; 8 \times 7$	(g)	j	m
14. $8 \times 4 \; < \; 8 \times 8$	(e)	t	a

Use the letters you circled to answer the question.

Who was the 30th President of the United States?

C   a   l   v   i   n

C   o   o   l   i   d   g   e

4.9 **PRACTICE** for pages 124–125

Dividing by 2, 4, and 8

Complete each number rocket. Start with the number in the circle. Follow the arrows to divide. Write each answer in the correct square. Divide again if there is another arrow. Write the last answer in any line of arrows in the heart shape. All the numbers in the hearts of each completed rocket should be the same.

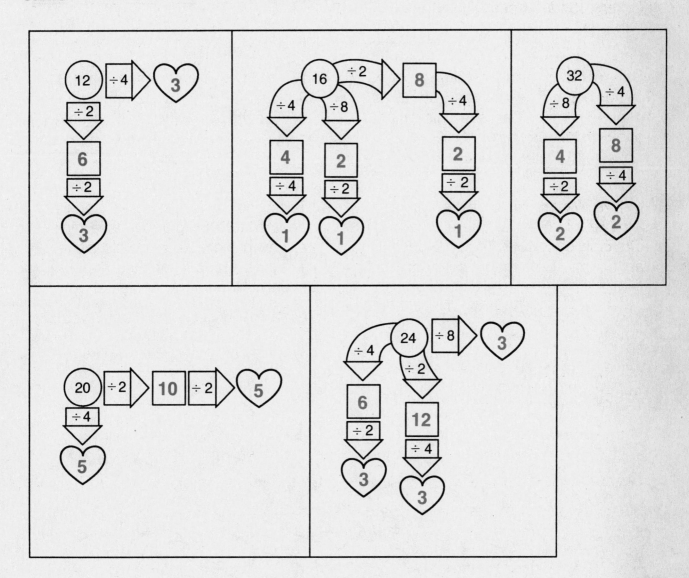

4.10 ▶ PRACTICE

for pages 126–127

Problem Solving Strategy: **Make a Plan**

Solve each problem. Make a plan when it helps.

1. Leonard wants to buy a shirt on which the letters of his first name have been sewn. A shirt costs $6. Letters costs $3 each. How much will the shirt cost in all? ___**$27**___

2. How much would the shirt cost if Leonard had used his nickname, Len? ___**$15**___

3. Didi wants to read the last 64 pages of her book. She can read about 20 pages an hour. Can she finish the book if she reads from 3:00 P.M. to 6:30 P.M.? ___**Yes, she can finish.**___

4. William has 2 quarters, 1 dime, and 3 nickels. If he buys 2 apples for 35¢ each, how much will he have left? ___**5 cents**___

5. In Mrs. Mott's class, desks are arranged in 5 rows. There are 6 desks in each row. Today 6 desks are empty. How many students are in class today? ___**24 students**___

6. Tess and 3 friends picked apples. Tess picked 8 apples, Jesse picked 4, Lou picked 10, and Lois picked 2. They decide to share the apples evenly. How many apples should each friend get? ___**6 apples each**___

4.11 PRACTICE

for pages 128–129

Multiplying and Dividing by 3 and 6

Write the answer. Use a pattern to help you. Find the answer under the line below. Write the letter of the answer on the line. The letters will spell the answer to the riddle.

1. $3 \times 6 = \underline{18}$ I

$6 \times 6 = \underline{36}$ T

2. $3 \times 1 = \underline{3}$ A

$6 \times 1 = \underline{6}$ A

3. $6 \times 7 = \underline{42}$ H

$3 \times 7 = \underline{21}$ T

4. $3 \times 5 = \underline{15}$ T

$6 \times 5 = \underline{30}$ N

5. $3 \times 8 = \underline{24}$ A

$6 \times 8 = \underline{48}$ S

6. $12 \div 6 = \underline{2}$ A

$12 \div 3 = \underline{4}$ S

7. $6 \times 9 = \underline{54}$ J

$3 \times 9 = \underline{27}$ I

8. $48 \div 3 = \underline{16}$ W

$48 \div 6 = \underline{8}$ U

9. $3 \times 4 = \underline{12}$ O

$6 \times 4 = \underline{24}$ A

10. $42 \div 6 = \underline{7}$ M

$42 \div 3 = \underline{14}$ L

What do you get when you cross a hyena with a parrot?

A   N   A   N   I   M   A   L   T   H   A   T
2   3   18 7   24 14 21   36

L   A   U   G   H   S   A   T   I   T   S   O   W   N
    6   8   42   24 15 27   4   16 30

J   O   K   E   S   .
54 12   48

4.12 PRACTICE for pages 130–131

Multiplying and Dividing by 7 and 9

All the number sentences in the puzzle are either division or multiplication sentences. Write the answer for each number sentence. Then color in red any puzzle piece with a 7 in it to find the answer to the riddle.

What can fit inside an open box but is never in a closed one?

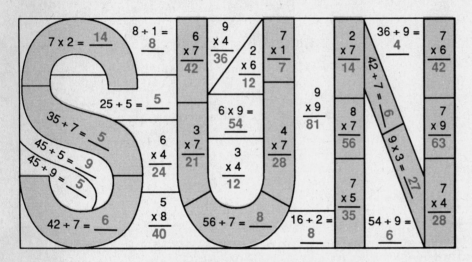

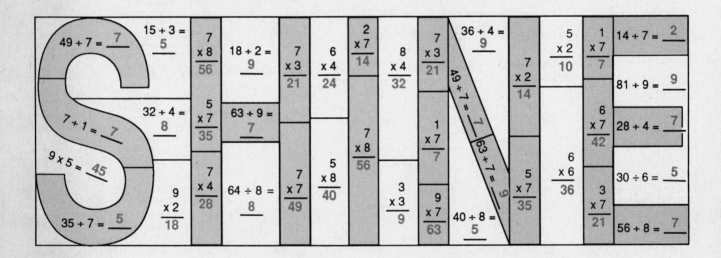

4.13 PRACTICE/RECORDING SHEET for pages 132–133

Multiples

Use the hundreds chart below to record the multiples.

1	2	3	4	5	6	7	8	9	10
11	12	13	14	15	16	17	18	19	20
21	22	23	24	25	26	27	28	29	30
31	32	33	34	35	36	37	38	39	40
41	42	43	44	45	46	47	48	49	50
51	52	53	54	55	56	57	58	59	60
61	62	63	64	65	66	67	68	69	70
71	72	73	74	75	76	77	78	79	80
81	82	83	84	85	86	87	88	89	90
91	92	93	94	95	96	97	98	99	100

1	2	3	4	5	6	7	8	9	10
11	12	13	14	15	16	17	18	19	20
21	22	23	24	25	26	27	28	29	30
31	32	33	34	35	36	37	38	39	40
41	42	43	44	45	46	47	48	49	50
51	52	53	54	55	56	57	58	59	60
61	62	63	64	65	66	67	68	69	70
71	72	73	74	75	76	77	78	79	80
81	82	83	84	85	86	87	88	89	90
91	92	93	94	95	96	97	98	99	100

1	2	3	4	5	6	7	8	9	10
11	12	13	14	15	16	17	18	19	20
21	22	23	24	25	26	27	28	29	30
31	32	33	34	35	36	37	38	39	40
41	42	43	44	45	46	47	48	49	50
51	52	53	54	55	56	57	58	59	60
61	62	63	64	65	66	67	68	69	70
71	72	73	74	75	76	77	78	79	80
81	82	83	84	85	86	87	88	89	90
91	92	93	94	95	96	97	98	99	100

1	2	3	4	5	6	7	8	9	10
11	12	13	14	15	16	17	18	19	20
21	22	23	24	25	26	27	28	29	30
31	32	33	34	35	36	37	38	39	40
41	42	43	44	45	46	47	48	49	50
51	52	53	54	55	56	57	58	59	60
61	62	63	64	65	66	67	68	69	70
71	72	73	74	75	76	77	78	79	80
81	82	83	84	85	86	87	88	89	90
91	92	93	94	95	96	97	98	99	100

1	2	3	4	5	6	7	8	9	10
11	12	13	14	15	16	17	18	19	20
21	22	23	24	25	26	27	28	29	30
31	32	33	34	35	36	37	38	39	40
41	42	43	44	45	46	47	48	49	50
51	52	53	54	55	56	57	58	59	60
61	62	63	64	65	66	67	68	69	70
71	72	73	74	75	76	77	78	79	80
81	82	83	84	85	86	87	88	89	90
91	92	93	94	95	96	97	98	99	100

1	2	3	4	5	6	7	8	9	10
11	12	13	14	15	16	17	18	19	20
21	22	23	24	25	26	27	28	29	30
31	32	33	34	35	36	37	38	39	40
41	42	43	44	45	46	47	48	49	50
51	52	53	54	55	56	57	58	59	60
61	62	63	64	65	66	67	68	69	70
71	72	73	74	75	76	77	78	79	80
81	82	83	84	85	86	87	88	89	90
91	92	93	94	95	96	97	98	99	100

4.14 PRACTICE/RECORDING SHEET for pages 134–135

Factors

1. _____ 24 _____

2. _____ No, there is no rectangle with 24 squares that _____
_____ has 5 squares on a side. _____

	Number	Factors	Common Factors
3.	24	1, 2, 3, 4, 6, 8, 12, 24	
4.	18	1, 2, 3, 6, 9, 18	
5.	24, 18		1, 2, 3, 6
6.	16	1, 2, 4, 8, 16	
7.	24,16		1, 2, 4, 8
8.	16, 18, 24		1, 2

Summing It Up

9. _____ Answers may vary but may include: because you can always divide a _____
_____ number (except 0) by itself. _____

10. _____ 2 _____

11. _____ yes, because 4 is a factor of 8 _____

12. _____ Answers may vary but may include: Try to write all the multiplication _____
_____ sentences with that number in the product. _____

4.15 ▧ PRACTICE/RECORDING SHEET for pages 136–137

Multiplication Patterns

Kind of Building	Number of Buildings of This Kind	Number of Blocks Per Building	Total Blocks Used

Answers will vary.

4.16 PRACTICE

Problem Solving: Using Strategies

Mrs. Bader is the new home economics teacher at Hartsdale School. She wants to order supplies from two catalogs. There are 28 students in the class.

Solve each problem. Use one of the strategies you have learned.

	Cookin' Kitchen	Kitchen Time
Wooden Spoons	$2 each $18 dozen	3 for $5
Mixing Bowls	$12 set of 3	$10 set of 3
Cookie Tins	$6 each $30 $\frac{1}{2}$ doz $50 doz	$6 each $9 for 2
Measuring Cups	$3 each set	$2 each set
Aprons	$7 for 3	$9 for 4

1. Mrs. Bader needs 1 set of bowls for every 7 students. How many sets must she order? ____**4 sets**____

2. Which company charges less for the bowls? ____**Kitchen Time**____

3. Mrs. Bader needs 1 cookie tin for every 3 students. How many tins must she order? ____**10 tins**____

4. Which company charges less for the number of tins she needs? How much will the cookie tins cost? **Kitchen Time; $45**

5. Students will work in groups of 4. Each group needs a set of measuring cups. How many sets of cups should be ordered? **7 sets**

6. From which company should Mrs. Bader order measuring cups? **Kitchen Time**

7. Each student needs at least 1 wooden spoon. There are already 6 spoons on hand. How many spoons should be ordered to get the lowest price? Which company should get the order? What will the cost be? **two dozen spoons from Cookin' Kitchen; $36**

8. Mrs. Bader can buy 30 yards of fabric for $35. Each student can make an apron with 1 yard of fabric. Is it cheaper to buy aprons or to make them? ____**to make them**____

4.17 PRACTICE

for pages 140–141

Mental Math: Division Patterns

Write the quotient for the division exercise in each rocket. Then find the division fact that helped you divide mentally. Draw a line from each rocket to the correct division fact.

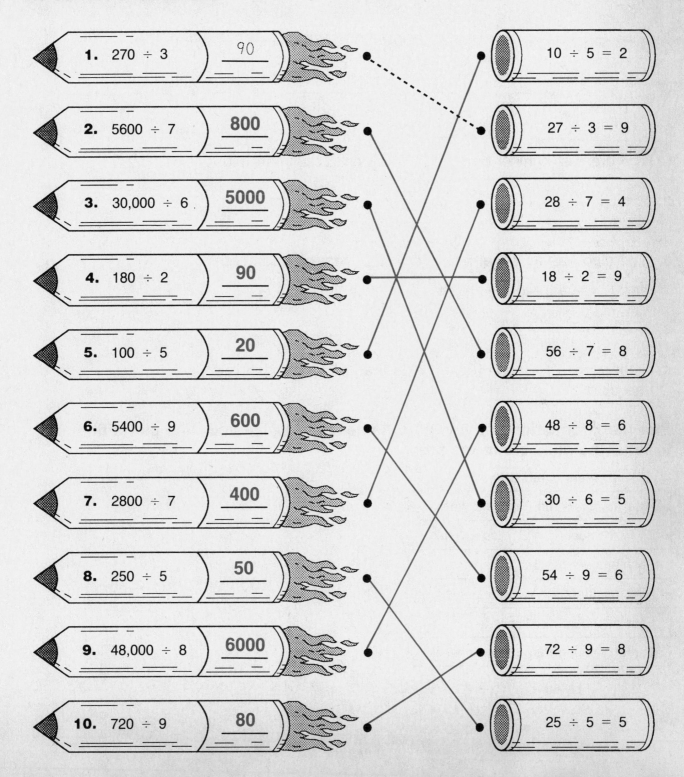

1. 270 ÷ 3 — 90

2. 5600 ÷ 7 — 800

3. 30,000 ÷ 6 — 5000

4. 180 ÷ 2 — 90

5. 100 ÷ 5 — 20

6. 5400 ÷ 9 — 600

7. 2800 ÷ 7 — 400

8. 250 ÷ 5 — 50

9. 48,000 ÷ 8 — 6000

10. 720 ÷ 9 — 80

10 ÷ 5 = 2

27 ÷ 3 = 9

28 ÷ 7 = 4

18 ÷ 2 = 9

56 ÷ 7 = 8

48 ÷ 8 = 6

30 ÷ 6 = 5

54 ÷ 9 = 6

72 ÷ 9 = 8

25 ÷ 5 = 5

4.18 PRACTICE

Special Topic: **Line Plots**

Use the line plot to answer the questions below.

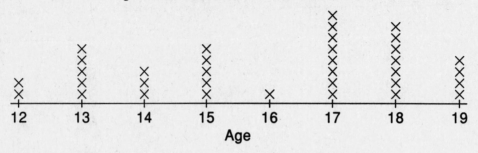

Ages of Members of the Runners' Club

Age

1. The greatest number of club members are __17__ years old.

2. A total of __10__ club members are 14 years old or younger.

3. The club has an equal number of __13__-year-old members and __15__-year-old members.

4. In all, there are __35__ members in the club.

5. There are __2__ more 18-year-olds than 15-year-olds in the club.

Plot the information in a line plot. Remember to give your line plot a title and to label the numbers in the scale.

Runners' Club Statistics

Nine members run 3 miles a week.
Eight members run 2 miles a week.
Six members run 5 miles a week.
Five members run 4 miles a week.
Four members run 1 mile a week.
Three members run 6 miles a week.

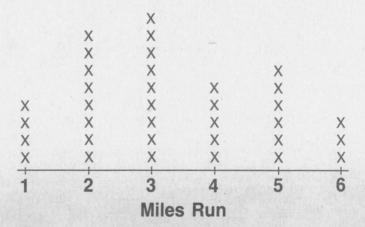

Number of Miles Run by Runners' Club Members in a Week

Miles Run

5.1 ▶PRACTICE
for pages 150–151

Flips

Write which figure is a flip image of the shaded figure.

1. _____c_____

 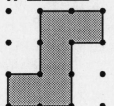 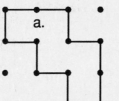 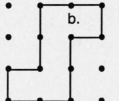 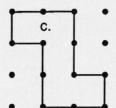 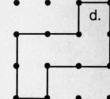

2. _____a, b_____

 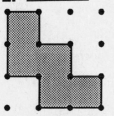 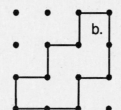 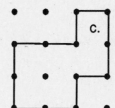 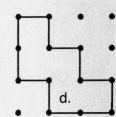

3. _____b_____

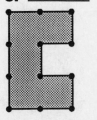 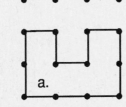 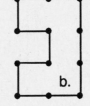 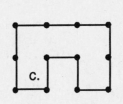 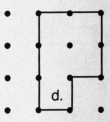

4. _____c or d_____

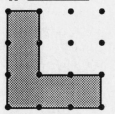 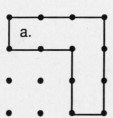 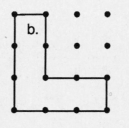 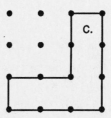 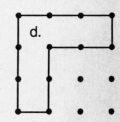

5. _____b_____

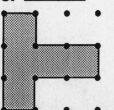 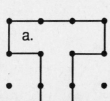 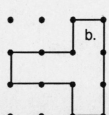 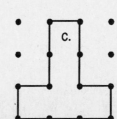 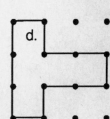

Turns

Write which figures could be turn images of the shaded figure.

1. ___b,c___

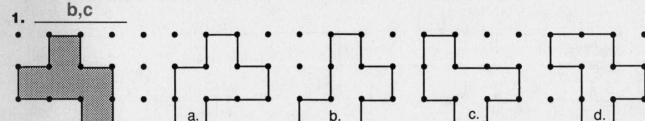

2. ___c,d___

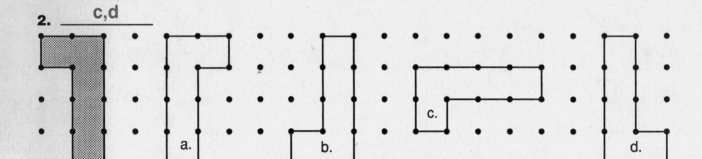

3. ___a,b,c,d___

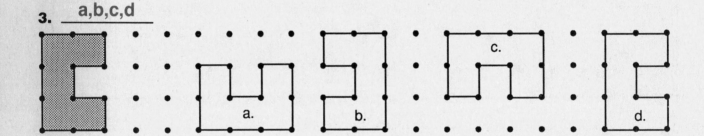

4. ___b,d___

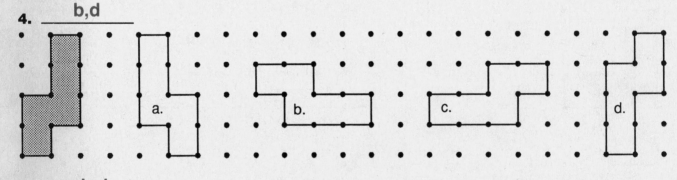

5. ___a,b,d___

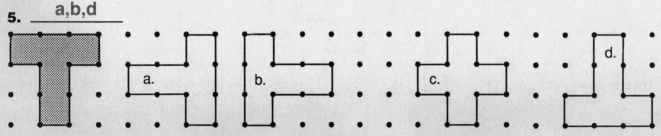

5.3 PRACTICE

for pages 154–155

Angles

Write *quarter turn*, *half turn*, or *three-quarter* turn to describe each turn of the hour hand on the clocks below.

1.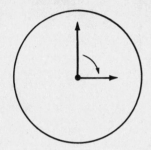

quarter turn

2.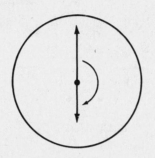

half turn

3.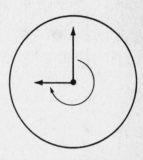

three-quarter turn

Write *90°*, *180°*, or *270°* to describe how many degrees are between the minute hand and the hour hand on each clock below.

4.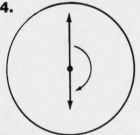

180°

5.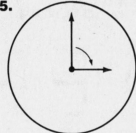

90°

6.

270°

7.

180°

8.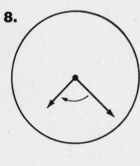

90°

9.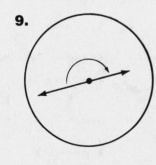

180°

10.

90°

11.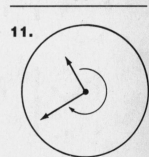

270°

12. How many degrees does the minute hand turn every hour? __360°__

13. If a right angle takes up 90 degrees of a circle, how many degrees is the rest of the circle? __270 degrees__

Symmetry

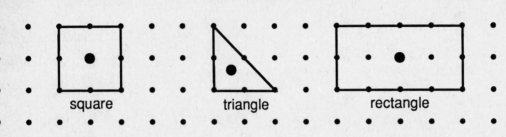

square   triangle   rectangle

circle   parallelogram   octagon

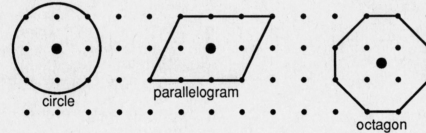

ABCDEF
GHIJKL
MNOPRST
UVWYZ

Name_____ Date_____

Problem Solving: **Make a Model**

Solve each problem. Make a model when it helps.

1. Mary wants to measure her waist using a ruler, string,

   and paper. How can she do that? <u>**She can measure her waist with the**</u>

   __**string and then measure its length using the ruler.**__

2. A table is 8 feet long and 4 feet
   wide. What is the greatest number of
   people who could sit at the table if
   each used a place mat 2 feet wide
   and 1 foot high? The place mats

   may touch. <u>**10 people**</u>

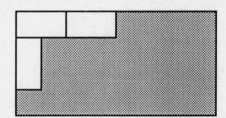

3. Danielle will cut 8 napkins from
   1 piece of square paper lace. All the
   napkins will be the same size. What
   is the least number of cuts she can

   make? <u>**4 cuts**</u>

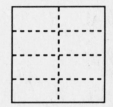

4. There are 6 bowls of flowers on the
   table. How can Danielle move only
   2 bowls to make a centerpiece that
   forms a circle?

   <u>**Move bowl 5 to touch 3 and 2.**</u>

   <u>**Move bowl 3 to touch 5 and 6.**</u>

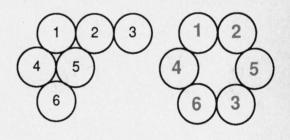

5. Lynn asked Fred to solve this
   puzzle: Remove 3 toothpicks to
   leave 3 triangles. Each of the
   toothpicks left should be part of a
   triangle. Cross out the toothpicks that
   Fred should remove.

6. Fred asked Lynn to solve this
   puzzle: Remove 6 toothpicks to
   leave 4 triangles that are all the
   same size. Cross out the toothpicks
   that Lynn should remove.

Answers may vary. One variation is shown.

5.6 ▸ PRACTICE

Slides

Draw a line to match each figure at the left with the same figure and its slide image at the right. The slide arrow shows the direction and the distance of the slide.

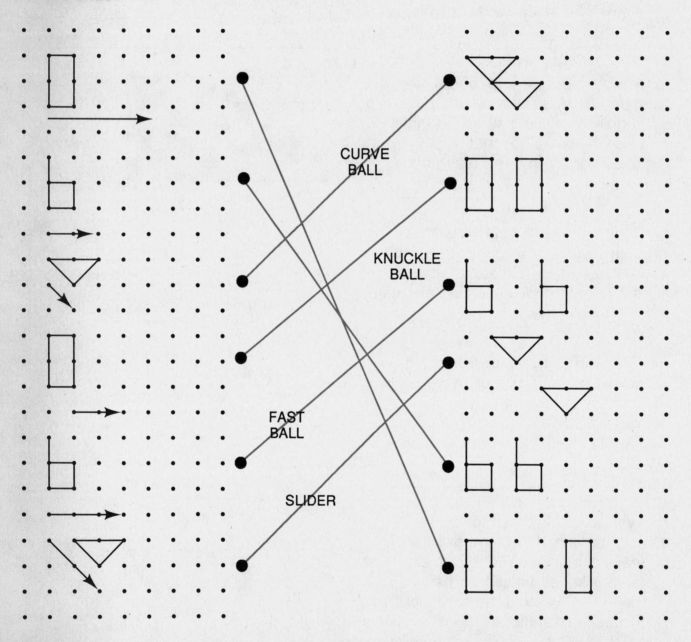

CURVE
BALL

KNUCKLE
BALL

FAST
BALL

SLIDER

On the line below, write the word or phrase that has not been crossed by any of the lines.

A ____knuckle ball____ is the name of a baseball pitch in which the ball does not spin after it has been thrown.

5.7 PRACTICE for pages 162–163

Ordered Pairs

Trace the route that Peggy took from her house to the school fair. Write all the corner points she crossed.

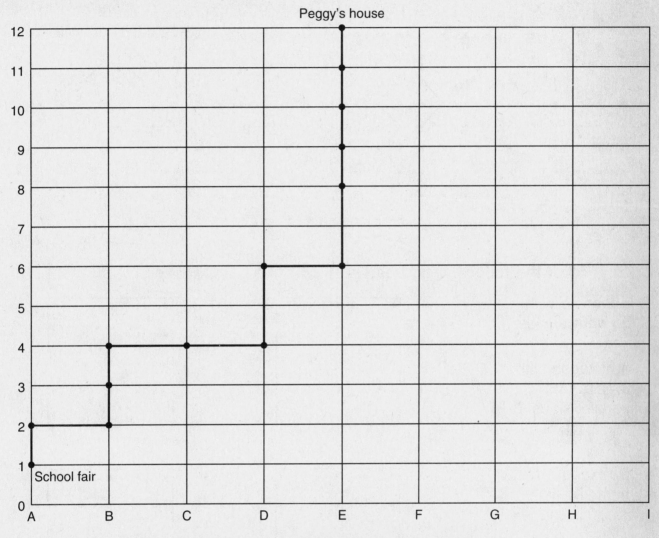

Peggy's route: <u>**E,12; E,11; E,10; E,9; E,8; E,6; D,6; D,4;**</u>
<u>**C,4; B,4; B,3; B,2; A,2; A,1**</u>

Each number below is part of one of the ordered pairs above.
Write the letter of the ordered pair on the line.
This is what Peggy's friend told her the day before the fair:

<u>**B**</u> <u>**E**</u> T H <u>**E**</u> R <u>**E**</u> O R B <u>**E**</u> S Q U A R <u>**E**</u> .
3   8   12   10   11   9

5.8 ▸PRACTICE   for pages 164–165

Quadrilaterals and Other Polygons

Copy each figure onto the dot paper below it. Then mark an *X* inside each right angle.

hexagon   octagon   pentagon   triangle

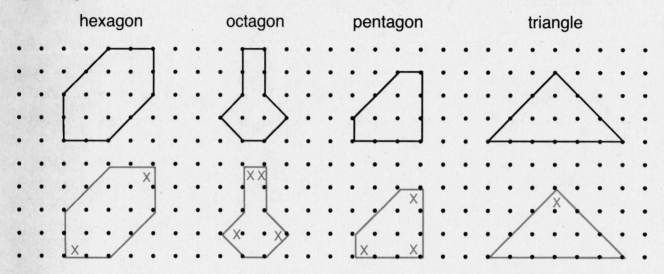

Draw each of the following figures: Sample answers shown.

1. a triangle with no right angles

2. a hexagon with 3 pairs of parallel sides

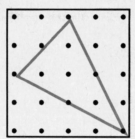
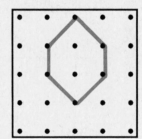

3. a hexagon with two right angles

4. a quadrilateral with no right angles

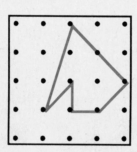
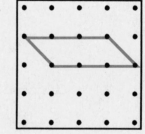

5. a pentagon with no parallel sides

6. an octagon with 4 pairs of parallel sides and no right angles

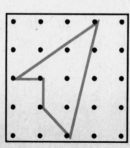
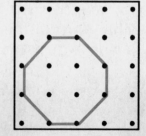

5.9 ▸ PRACTICE

Problem Solving: Using Strategies

Solve each problem.

1. Start at Lasso Road and 2nd Street. Go north 1 block, and then go east 1 block.

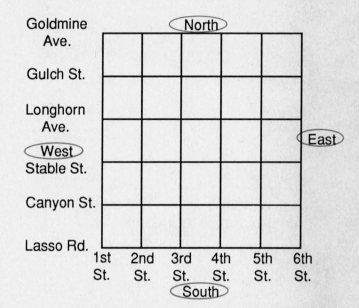

   a. Where are you?

   Canyon Street and 3rd Street

   b. Which way are you facing?

   east

2. Now go north 2 blocks. Go east 2 blocks. Go south 1 block. Where are you? Stable Street and 5th Street

3. The Eureka Gold Museum is located at Gulch Street and 2nd Street. How can you get there from 5th Street and Longhorn Avenue? Answers may vary but may include: Go 1 block north and 3 blocks west.

4. Suppose you are at the Eureka Gold Museum. Write directions from there to Canyon Street and 4th Street.
   Answers may vary but may include: Walk 2 blocks east and 3 blocks south.

5. On the map, draw a park. Write directions about how to get from the park to the Eureka Gold Museum.
   Answers may vary.

6. What is the shortest route from Goldmine Avenue and 5th Street to Stable Street and 2nd Street? No shortest route—All of them contain 6 blocks.

5.10 PRACTICE

for pages 168–169

Counting Squares

Write how many squares each figure contains.

1.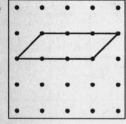

3 squares

2.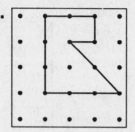

6 squares

3.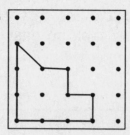

$5\frac{1}{2}$ squares

4.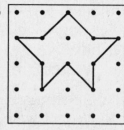

5 squares

The figure at the right contains $8\frac{1}{2}$ squares.

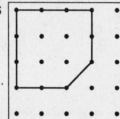

Draw three different figures, each containing $8\frac{1}{2}$ squares. **Answers may vary.**

5.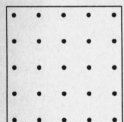

6.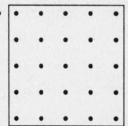

7.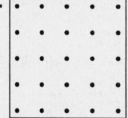

Draw three different figures, each containing 10 squares. **Answers may vary.**

8.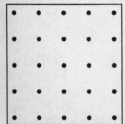

9.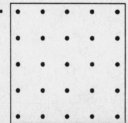

10.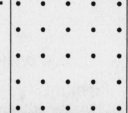

5.11 PRACTICE

Area

Each figure below is shown on centimeter squared paper.
Write the area of each figure. Then use a ruler to draw a straight line to connect the figures with equal areas.

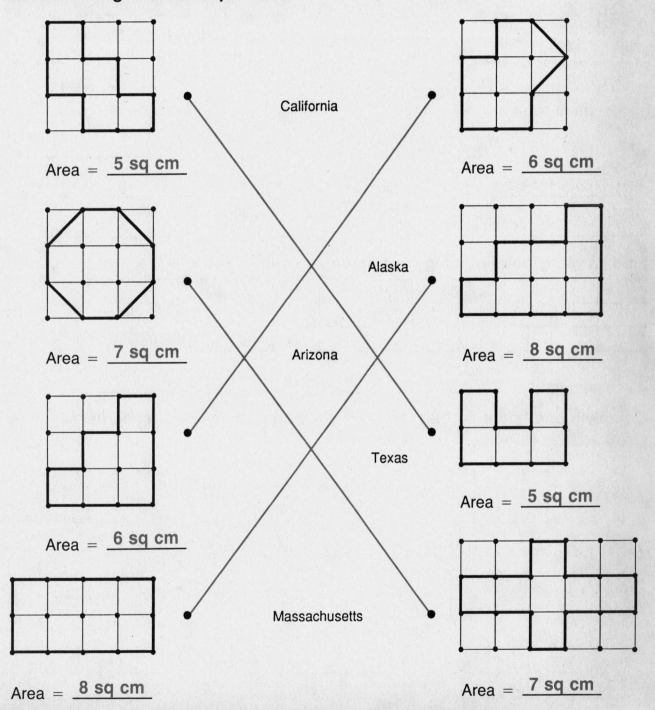

Area = __5 sq cm__

Area = __6 sq cm__

California

Alaska

Area = __7 sq cm__

Arizona

Area = __8 sq cm__

Texas

Area = __6 sq cm__

Area = __5 sq cm__

Massachusetts

Area = __8 sq cm__

Area = __7 sq cm__

Write the name of the state that is enclosed by the parallelogram.

Which state is just slightly smaller than Italy? __Arizona__

5.12 ▶PRACTICE

for pages 172–173

Congruence and Similarity

Find three pairs of congruent figures below. Tell whether they are related by a slide, a flip, or a turn.

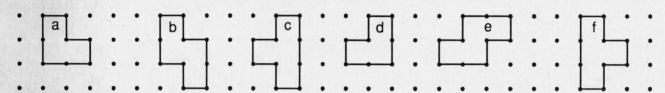

congruent pairs   related by

1. _____a and d_____   a flip or a turn

2. _____b and e_____   a turn

3. _____c and f_____   a flip or a turn

Find as many pairs of congruent figures as you can.

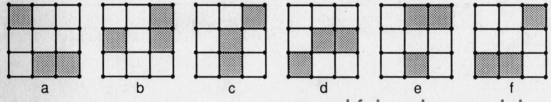

a   b   c   d   e   f

4. Congruent figures: ___a and f; b and e; c and d___

Complete one figure so that the two figures in each pair are congruent.

5.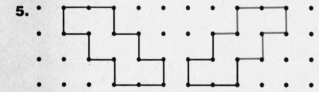

6.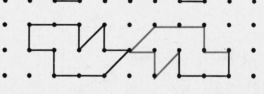

7.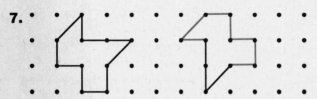

8.

9.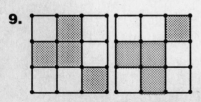

10.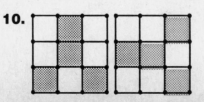

11.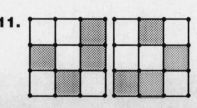

Answers may vary. A sample is given.

5.13 PRACTICE/RECORDING SHEET for pages 174–175

Solids

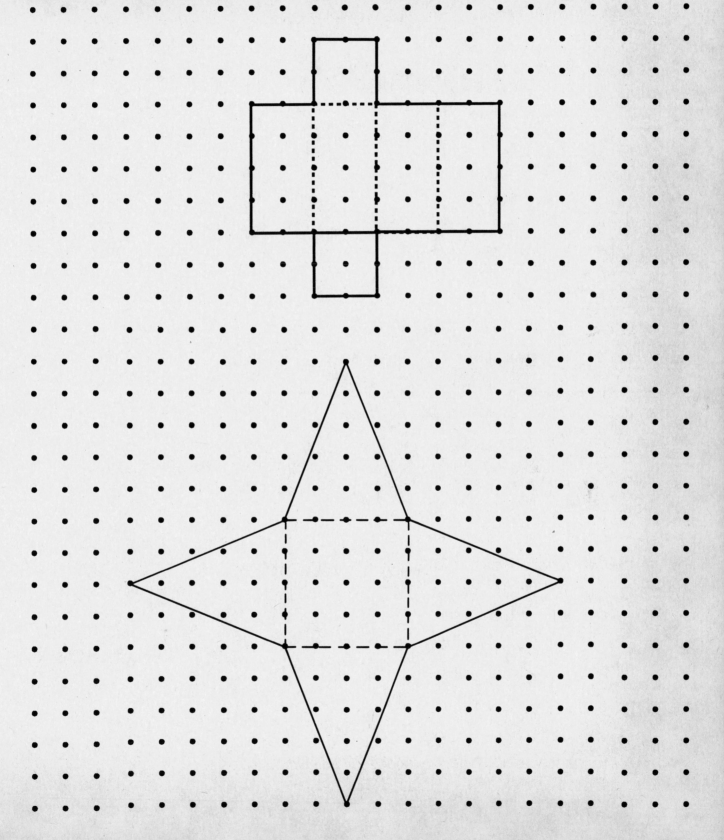

Visualization

Draw line segments to show all single cubes.

1.

2.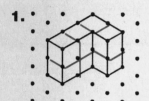

3.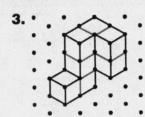

4.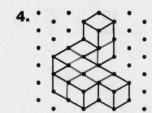

5.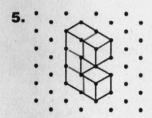

6.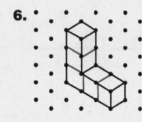

7.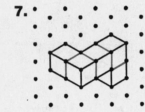

8.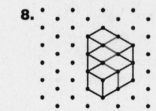

9. Which of the drawings above are pentacubes?

5, 6, 7, 8

You can make the rectangular prism at the right from 2 different pentacubes and 2 single cubes.

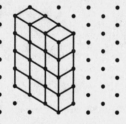

Here are the pentacubes you can choose from to make the prism.

a.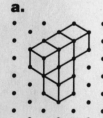

b.

c.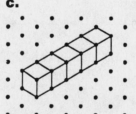

d.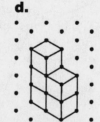

e.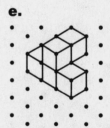

10. Which 2 pentacubes would you choose? __a, b or b, d__

11. Build the prism with cubes.

5.15 PRACTICE/RECORDING SHEET for pages 178–179

Volume

1. _____

2. _____

3. _____

4. _____

5. _____

6. _____

7. _____

8. _____

9. _____

10. _____

11. _____

12. _____

Number of Cubes (Volume)	Number of Cubes High	Number of Squares on Top	Area on Top
24	4	13. 6	14. 6
24	2	15. 12	16. 12
24	3	17. 8	18. 8
20	5	4	4
20	1	20	20
20	4	5	5

5.16 ▸ PRACTICE

for page 180

Problem Solving: Using Strategies

Solve each problem. Use one of the strategies you have learned.

1. Gerry wants to display his karate medals. The medals are 4 inches long and 2 inches wide. He wants to have 2 inches between each medal and 2 inches between a medal and the inside frame of the display case. The display case, including the 1-inch wooden frame on each side, is 20 inches wide. How many medals can Gerry fit across in the display case? _____ **4 medals** _____

2. The same case is 15 inches long, including the 1-inch wooden frame on each side. Gerry wants to have 2 inches between rows of medals. He also wants 2 inches between either end of each row and the frame. Will two rows of medals fit? **No, the display case is one inch** _____ **short.**

3. Gerry decides to leave only 1 inch between the rows of medals. Will 2 rows fit now? _____ **yes** _____

4. Gerry has a picture of himself in his karate uniform. The picture is 5 inches wide by 7 inches high. What is the area of the picture? _____ **35 square inches** _____

5. Gerry has red cardboard that is 6 inches high and 6 inches wide. What is the area of the cardboard? _____ **36 square inches** _____

6. Will Gerry's picture fit on the cardboard? Explain. _____ **No, the picture is 1 inch taller than the** _____ **cardboard.**

6.1 PRACTICE   for pages 188–189

Estimating Products

Underline the front-end estimate. Then circle the letter of the rounded estimate. They will be the same sometimes. Use the letters you circled to solve the riddle below.

1. 6 × 325   **a.** 3600   **b.** 1850   **(c.)** 1800

2. 3 × 709   **(e.)** 2100   **f.** 2200   **g.** 2300

3. 4 × 867   **j.** 3200   **(k.)** 3600   **l.** 4000

4. 9 × 892   **(c.)** 8100   **d.** 8900   **e.** 7200

5. 5 × 634   **(h.)** 3000   **i.** 3300   **j.** 3500

6. 2 × 9920   **r.** 9000   **s.** 18,000   **(t.)** 20,000

7. 6 × 5881   **d.** 30,000   **(e.)** 36,000   **f.** 3600

8. 8 × 2344   **g.** 1600   **(h.)** 16,000   **i.** 160,000

9. 7 × 9846   **h.** 63,000   **(i.)** 70,000   **j.** 77,000

10. 4 × 6214   **(e.)** 24,000   **f.** 28,000   **g.** 28,500

11. 9 × 5326   **r.** 54,000   **s.** 50,000   **(t.)** 45,000

12. 5 × 7795   **q.** 35,000   **r.** 37,000   **(s.)** 40,000

13. 8 × 7408   **(r.)** 56,000   **s.** 64,000   **t.** 6400

What should you learn to do before you ride a bike?

    k   t   i e s

c   h   e   c   k   t   h   e   t   i   r   e   s
1   5   2   4   3   6   8   7   11 9   13 10 12

(4) **79**

6.2 ▸ PRACTICE

for pages 190–191

Multiplying with Array Diagrams

Match the problem in column A with its array in column B and with the product in column C.

A.

1. 21
   × 2

2. 32
   × 5

3. 65
   × 4

4. 24
   × 6

5. 48
   × 8

6. 66
   × 7

7. 29
   × 3

8. 53
   × 9

9. 56
   × 6

B.

30	2
20	1
40	8
20	9
60	5
50	3
20	4
60	6
50	6

5, 2, 8, 3, 4, 9, 6, 7, 6

C.

260
87
42
160
144
384
462
336
477

6.3 ▸ PRACTICE

Multiplying 2-Digit Numbers

Find the missing number by multiplying. Write it in the targets. Use mental math when you can.

1.

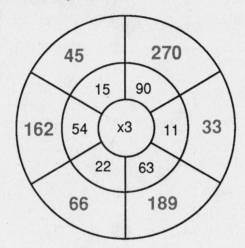

2.

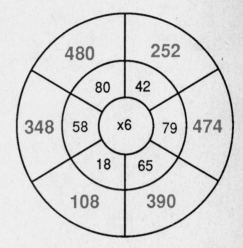

3.

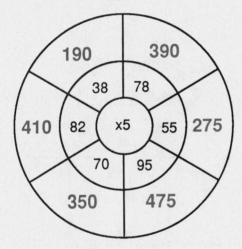

4.

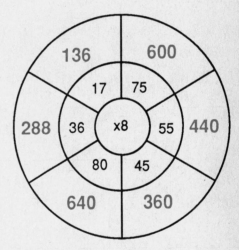

5.

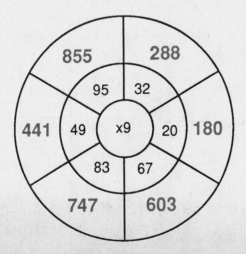

6.

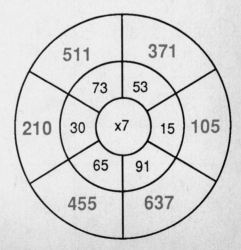

6.4 ▶ PRACTICE

for pages 194–195

Multiplying 3-Digit Numbers

Write the product. Then draw an X through the product in the maze below. Your X's will trace a path from START to FINISH.

1.	2.	3.	4.	5.
758 $\times\ 7$ 5306	74 $\times\ 6$ 444	41 $\times\ 7$ 287	409 $\times\ 8$ 3272	257 $\times\ 9$ 2313

6.	7.	8.	9.	10.
750 $\times\ 3$ 2250	503 $\times\ 6$ 3018	352 $\times\ 6$ 2112	63 $\times\ 3$ 189	505 $\times\ 3$ 1515

11.	12.	13.	14.	15.
572 $\times\ 4$ 2288	82 $\times\ 7$ 574	409 $\times\ 3$ 1227	309 $\times\ 6$ 1854	41 $\times\ 9$ 369

16.	17.	18.	19.	20.
758 $\times\ 6$ 4548	1182 $\times\ 5$ 5910	907 $\times\ 7$ 6349	117 $\times\ 3$ 351	37 $\times\ 9$ 333

328	3032	1227	1854	1515	944	818	1892	5828	444	4548	2313	FINISH
205	826	2288	1760	333	5910	3710	164	1584	574	2816	2752	1814
410	656	2250	329	1928	287	3626	492	2628	369	3790	7256	3274
START	5306	6349	374	1408	3018	3272	351	189	2112	4535	1632	4328

6.5 ◥ **PRACTICE**   for pages 196–197

··

Problem Solving Strategy: **Guess and Check**

Solve each problem. Use the guess and check strategy to help you.

1. At the amusement park, these 6 children are waiting to go on the "Twister" ride. Each car can hold 300 pounds. Which children should ride together? __**Answers may vary.**__

Sara, Dan, Meg;
Len, Luis, and Beth

Beth
85
pounds

Dan
120
pounds

Meg
60
pounds

Sara
110
pounds

Len
100
pounds

Luis
105
pounds

2. Kendell's Department Store wants to place an order for children's summer hats. Each hat costs $3. How many hats can Kendell's order for $435?
145 hats

3. At the farmer's market, Helen bought 3 pounds of tomatoes and a head of lettuce for $4.59. The lettuce cost $1.47. What was the price of a pound of tomatoes? __**$1.04**__

4. The sum of the numbers 11, 12, and 13 is 36. What three numbers in order have a sum of 3 times 10?
The numbers 9, 10, and 11
have a sum of 30.

5. Michael had 10 coins of the same value in his pocket. Then he lost 60¢. What were the coins? How much does Michael have left?
They were dimes; he has 40¢
left.

6. If you subtracted 33 from the mystery number, the result would be double 33 or the mystery number upside down. What is the mystery number? __**99**__

7. John the baker made 3 batches of bread. He used 177 ounces of soy flour. How much soy flour is in each batch of bread? __**59 ounces**__

6.6 ▸ PRACTICE

for page 198

Choose a Computation Method: Exact or Estimate

Use the picture to tell whether each problem needs an estimate or an exact answer. You do not have to write the answers to the problems.

1.

> 8 workers at the plant store each prepare 12 gift baskets

Order List

75 gift baskets have been ordered

a. Can the plant store fill all its orders for baskets?
_____estimate_____

b. How many baskets will be left when all orders have been filled?
_____exact answer_____

c. Suppose 4 more people order baskets. Can the store still fill all its orders? ___estimate___

2.

Catalogs We Have
1235 just printed
2483 on hand

Catalogs Ordered by Shoppers
1289 by mail
1711 by phone

a. What is the total number of catalogs ordered?
_____exact answer_____

b. How many more catalogs were ordered by phone than by mail?
_____exact answer_____

c. Can the store send a catalog to every shopper who ordered one?
_____estimate_____

3.

Mr. Yang's Bill

$8.95   plants
$4.52   soil
$4.89   seeds
This includes tax.

a. How much must Mr. Yang pay in all? _____exact answer_____

b. Does he have enough money to pay for what he bought?
_____estimate_____

c. How much change will he receive? _____exact answer_____

4.

> I earn $8.25 an hour. I worked 6 hours today.

$45, including tax

a. How much has Jo earned for today's work? ___exact answer___

b. Has she earned enough to buy the boots? ___estimate___

c. How much money will Jo have left? _____exact answer_____

6.7 ▸ PRACTICE

for pages 200–201

Multiplying 4-Digit Numbers

Write the product. Use the products to complete the puzzle.

A 2	B 7	C 6	D 5	E 5	■	F 2	G 4	H 3
I 4	5	4	1	4	■	J 6	5	6
K 3	3	6	8	■	L 3	8	8	8
M 8	0	7	■	N 4	3	2	1	6
■	■	O 2	9	9	7	■	■	4
P 7	Q 2	■		R 5	3	1	S 2	■
■	T 5	3	0	6	0	■	U 7	8

Across

A 5531 × 5 **P** 8 × 9

F 27 × 9 **R** 664 × 8

I 5046 × 9 **T** 7580 × 7

J 82 × 8 **U** 26 × 3

K 842 × 4

L 486 × 8

M 807 × 1

N 5402 × 8

O 333 × 9

Down

A 1219 × 2 **N** 826 × 6

B 1506 × 5 **Q** 5 × 5

C 8084 × 8 **S** 9 × 3

D 74 × 7

E 9 × 6

F 447 × 6

G 509 × 9

H 6144 × 6

L 6746 × 5

Name_____ Date_____

Problem Solving: Using Strategies

The Shea School is planning a mosaic for the school entrance. The mosaic will be made from small square tiles. The lettering will be done in blue tiles and the background in white tiles. The mosaic will read, "The Shea School"

Solve each problem. You may use a calculator.

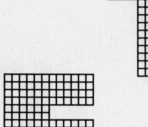
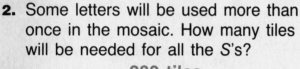
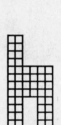

1. How many tiles will be used in the letter *T*? (HINT: Use multiplication so that you do not have to count every tile.) _____ **88 tiles** _____

2. Some letters will be used more than once in the mosaic. How many tiles will be needed for all the *S*'s?
   _____ **280 tiles** _____

3. How many tiles will be needed for all the *h*'s? _____ **168 tiles** _____

4. How many tiles will be needed for all the *o*'s? _____ **80 tiles** _____

5. How many tiles will be needed for all the *e*'s? _____ **72 tiles** _____

6. Knowing that there will be the same number of tiles in an *a* as in an *e*, 32 tiles in a *c*, and 14 in an *l*, how many tiles will be needed for all the lettering in the sign?
   _____ **770 tiles** _____

7. The whole sign will need 3432 tiles. How many of them will be white? (HINT: Use the number you found in exercise 6. Remember that the sign will have blue letters on a white background.) _____ **2662 white tiles** _____

6.9 PRACTICE

Multiplying Money

Streamside School needs to raise money for a new computer. The class that raises the most money wins a prize.

Solve each problem. Use a calculator to help you. Use the letters from the answers to solve the riddle.

1. How much did Ms. Tulio's class earn from each item sold?

8 cakes at $14.85 each _____ $118.80 _____ O

5 pencil cases at $1.62 _____ $8.10 _____ A

9 hand-painted mugs at $4.31 each _____ $38.79 _____ F

7 boxes of crayons at $1.35 each _____ $9.45 _____ Z

2. How much did Mr. Cruz's class earn from each item sold?

8 bags of cookies at $0.95 each _____ $7.60 _____ R

9 bags of nuts and raisins at $1.85 each _____ F

_____ $16.65 _____

2 portrait drawings at $12.30 each _____ $24.60 _____ E

5 chairs at $17.45 each _____ $87.25 _____ I

3. How much did Ms. May's class earn from each item sold?

5 leather belts at $20.75 each _____ $103.75 _____ O

4 ties at $19.80 each _____ $79.20 _____ P

7 packages of hair bands at $2.83 each _____ A

_____ $19.81 _____

8 recipe books at $6.76 each _____ $54.08 _____ T

4. The class that raised the most money won a

Z	O	O		T	R	I	P
$9.45	$118.80	$103.75		$54.08	$7.60	$87.25	$79.20

6.10 ▸ PRACTICE

Problem Solving: Using Strategies

Carl and his family live at the seashore. Every summer, they open a little store in their house.

Solve each problem. Use one of the strategies you have learned. Estimate when you can.

We've Got-It-All Price List	
suntan lotion—4 ounces	$6.49
suntan lotion—16 ounces	$19.95
beach hats children's	$3.59
adult's	$7.95
beach umbrella	$14.95
Rentals: beach towel per day	$2.00

1. Mrs. Smith wants to buy at least 12 ounces of suntan lotion. Should she buy 3 small bottles or 1 large bottle? Explain. __One large bottle; for a few cents more, she'll get 4 more ounces.__

2. Mr. Ruiz wants to buy a hat and a small bottle of suntan lotion and to rent a beach towel. About how much will he have left if he pays with a $20 bill? __He'll have about $3.50 left.__

3. Carl's family pays $12 for each beach towel. How many times must Carl rent one before he breaks even? __6 times__

4. On his day off, Carl wants to swim, look for shells, make a sand castle, and play softball. In how many different orders can he do these activities? __24 different orders__

5. Candy's parents plan to buy and share one beach umbrella. Will that cost less than buying two adult beach hats? __Yes, 2 hats are $17.90.__

6. Carl's family store is opened from noon until 6:00 PM, Monday through Friday and 9:00 AM to 6:00 PM on Saturday. How many hours is the store opened during the week? __39 hours__

Name_____ Date_____

7.1 PRACTICE

for pages 214–215

Division with Remainders

Divide. Write the remainder of each exercise in the box of the next exercise. The first one has been done for you.

1. 8)70 = 8 R6

2. 6 R3 → [6])39

3. 6 R4 → 5) [3] 4

4. 6 R1 → [4])25

5. 5 R6 → 7)4 [1]

6. 8 R4 → [6])52

7. 4 R8 → 9)4 [4]

8. 7 R7 → [8])63

9. 6 R3 → 4)2 [7]

10. 5 R3 → 6)3 [3]

11. 9 R2 → [3])29

12. 9 R1 → [2])19

13. 6 R3 → 8)5 [1]

14. 4 R3 → 5)2 [3]

15. 3 R5 → 6)2 [3]

16. 5 R5 → 9) [5] 0

17. 7 R6 → 7)5 [5]

18. 6 R2 → 4)2 [6]

19. 5 R2 → 6)3 [2]

20. 6 R4 → 8)5 [2]

21. 7 R5 → 6) [4] 7

© D.C. Heath and Company

(4) **89**

Understanding Remainders

When you divide, you can use the remainder, drop the remainder, or include the remainder in the answer by writing the next whole number.

Solve each problem. Circle the letter of the way you used the remainder.

1. Chairs for the chorus are set up in rows of 8. If the chorus has 55 members, how many rows of chairs are there? _____**7 rows**_____

   C   Use the remainder.

   S   Drop the remainder.

   (W)   Include the remainder.

2. The dance class has been formed into groups of 4. If there are 21 dancers in the class, how many dancers are not in a group?

   1 dancer
   _____

   (A)   Use the remainder.

   N   Drop the remainder.

   T   Include the remainder.

3. Josh is putting 76 stamps into an album. Each page holds 8 stamps. How many pages can Josh fill completely?

   9 pages
   _____

   R   Use the remainder.

   (V)   Drop the remainder.

   P   Include the remainder.

4. How many cars will be needed to take 33 students on a field trip if each car can take 5 students?

   7 cars
   _____

   I   Use the remainder.

   B   Drop the remainder.

   (E)   Include the remainder.

5. Miranda baked 48 cookies. She gave an equal number to each of 9 friends and the rest to her teacher. How many cookies did Miranda give her teacher?

   3 cookies
   _____

   (S)   Use the remainder.   C   Drop the remainder.   F   Include the remainder.

Write the letters you circled on the lines to solve the riddle.

What does the ocean say to the shore?

Nothing, it just __w__ __a__ __v__ __e__ __s__ .
           1   2   3   4   5

7.3 PRACTICE

Estimating Quotients

Estimate the quotient. Use your ruler. Draw a line from the dot after each exercise to the dot before the two multiples of 10 or 100 that your estimate is between. The letters that have not been crossed out spell the answer to the riddle at the bottom of the page.

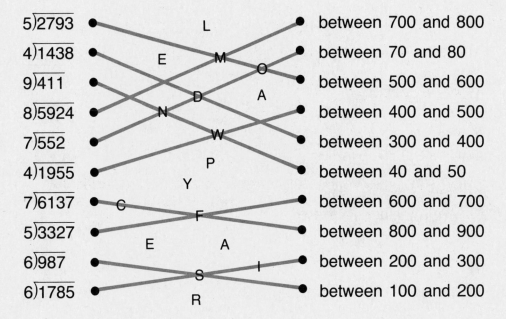

5)2793   •   between 700 and 800
4)1438   •   between 70 and 80
9)411   •   between 500 and 600
8)5924   •   between 400 and 500
7)552   •   between 300 and 400
4)1955   •   between 40 and 50
7)6137   •   between 600 and 700
5)3327   •   between 800 and 900
6)987   •   between 200 and 300
6)1785   •   between 100 and 200

What is a good year for kangaroos?

___ ___ ___ ___   ___ ___ ___ ___
 L   E   A   P   Y   E   A   R

7.4 PRACTICE

Two-Digit Quotients

Divide.

1. 14 R2
9)128

2. 11
4)44

3. 54 R1
9)487

4. 12 R3
6)75

5. 95 R2
8)762

6. 61 R1
7)428

7. 92 R3
9)831

8. 48
3)144

9. 82 R5
6)497

10. 77 R3
4)311

11. 83 R3
7)584

12. 52 R2
5)262

13. 82 R3
8)659

14. 71 R4
9)643

15. 97 R2
3)293

In the secret code, find the letters that match the quotients.
On the lines below, write each letter above the exercise
number to answer the question.

Code

N	M	A	U	A	E	E	S
11	12 R3	14 R2	95 R2	54 R1	92 R3	82 R5	61 R1

M	P	N	T	K	A	R	
48	52 R2	77 R3	83 R3	97 R2	82 R3	71 R4	

Where must you go to catch the spy named Rollercoaster?

A	N		A	M	U	S	E	M	E	N	T
1	2		3	4	5	6	7	8	9	10	11

P	A	R	K
12	13	14	15

7.5 ▶ PRACTICE

for pages 222–223

....

Problem Solving Strategy: Make Notes

Complete the notes. Then solve each problem.

1. The Young Astronauts Club will visit the NASA Space Center. The van rental will cost $72. Lunch at the center costs $4 per person. If 9 club members share the costs, how much will each member spend? ___**$12**___

> *Cost*
> Van $72
> Lunch $ 4 per person
> People

2. Club members held a bake sale to try to raise $72 for the van rental. They sold 8 cakes at $5.00 each. How much money do they still need to meet their goal? ___**$32**___

> Cake Price $5.00
> Cakes Sold   8
> Goal

3. Fred walks dogs 3 days a week to earn extra money for the trip. He gets paid $5.50 a day. From one-week's salary, Fred pays $12, his share of the cost of the trip. How much does he have left? ___**$4.50**___

> Earns $5.50 per day
> Works   days
> Spends

4. Club members arrived at the space center 4 hours after they left their clubhouse. On the 156-mile trip, they stopped for breakfast for 1 hour. How many miles per hour did their van average? ___**52 miles per hour**___

> Distance   156 miles
> Total Time   4 hours
> Time for Breakfast   1 hour

5. Club members arrived at 9:30 A.M. They spent 1 hour meeting with other clubs from around the country. Then they listened to half-hour talks given by an astronaut, a mission specialist, an engineer, a doctor, and a scientist. Then they stopped for lunch. What time did they stop for lunch? ___**1:00 P.M.**___

> Time Arrived   9:30 A.M.
> Number of Speakers
> Length of Each Talk

7.6 ▸ PRACTICE

Three-Digit Quotients

Divide. Use the digits in the boxes to complete the puzzle.

Across

A [1] [2] [8]
6) 7 6 8

C [5] [1] R2
9) 4 6 1

D [1] [4] R3
5) 7 3

F [9] [8] [1] R2
4) 3 9 2 6

H [6] [2] [9]
8) 5 0 3 2

I [9] [3] [7] R8
9) 8 4 4 1

L [9] [9]
6) 5 9 4

Down

A [1] [5] [1] R3
5) 7 5 8

B [2] [1] [4]
8) 1 7 1 2

E [9] [1] R4
6) 5 5 0

G [8] [4] [2]
7) 5 8 9 4

H [6] [7] [9] R3
4) 2 7 1 9

J [3] [9] R6
7) 2 7 9

K [7] [9] [2] R4
5) 3 9 6 4

Puzzle grid:

A **1**	B **2**	**8**
C **5**	**1**	■
D **1**	**4**	■
■	■	E **9**
F **9**	G **8**	**1**
■	**4**	■
H **6**	**2**	**9**
7	■	■
I **9**	J **3**	K **7**
■	L **9**	**9**

7.7 ◤ PRACTICE

for page 226

....

Problem Solving: **Using Strategies**

Solve each problem.

1. The Hartsdale Elementary School library bought 210 books. Of these, 70 will become part of the library collection, and the rest will be sold at the annual book fair. If each book was sold at a $2 profit, how much did the library earn? _____**$280**_____

2. Chester borrowed money for his new bike. He owes his mother $50 and his father $40. If he paid back $15 each week, how long did it take him to pay back his parents? _____**6 weeks**_____

3. Julie is putting photos in a photo album. Each page is 12 inches long and 15 inches wide. How many 3-inch long and 4-inch wide photos can she put on a page of the album? _____**12 photos**_____

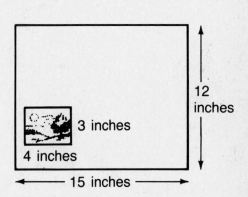

12 inches

3 inches

4 inches

◄——— 15 inches ———►

4. Julie has some photos that are 4 inches long and 3 inches wide. How many of these will fit on a page of the photo album? _____**15 photos**_____

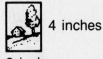

4 inches

3 inches

5. Julie has some photos that are 5 inches long and 7 inches wide. How many of these can she fit on one page of the photo album? _____**4 photos**_____

5 inches

7 inches

6. Leo works in a toy factory. He has to make 180 game pieces for one order and 240 game pieces for another order. If Leo makes 75 game pieces each day, will he complete both orders in 5 days? _____**no**_____

7.8 ▶ **PRACTICE**

Zeros in the Quotient

Divide. Use pencil and paper or mental math. Color each section that has a quotient without a remainder. Find out what the lifeguard found under the blanket.

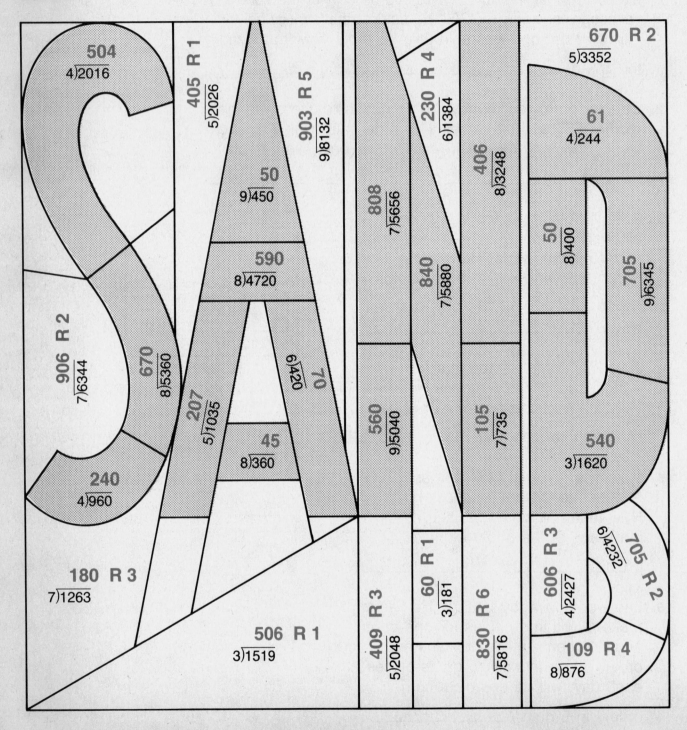

504
4)2016

405 R 1
5)2026

903 R 5
9)8132

230 R 4
6)1384

670 R 2
5)3352

50
9)450

61
4)244

808
7)5656

406
8)3248

590
8)4720

906 R 2
7)6344

670
8)5360

840
7)5880

50
8)400

705
9)6345

207
5)1035

70
6)420

560
9)5040

105
7)735

45
8)360

240
4)960

540
3)1620

180 R 3
7)1263

606 R 3
4)2427

705 R 2
6)4232

506 R 1
3)1519

409 R 3
5)2048

60 R 1
3)181

830 R 6
7)5816

109 R 4
8)876

7.9 PRACTICE/RECORDING SHEET for pages 230–231

Divisibility

1. _____

_____

2. _____

_____

4. _____

5. _____

_____

7. _____

_____

8. _____

10. _____

Divide to discover which numbers are divisible by 3, 2, and 5. Write *yes* or *no*.

Number	Divisible by 3	Number	Divisible by 2	Number	Divisible by 5
7	no	43	no	30	yes
15	yes	86	yes	55	yes
14	no	57	no	74	no
29	no	117	no	100	yes
72	yes	71	no	27	no
321	yes	32	yes	125	yes
43	no	33	no	41	no
37	no	64	yes	86	no
84	yes	29	no	115	yes
42	yes	120	yes	80	yes
32	no	98	yes	130	yes
235	no	56	yes	65	yes

7.10 ▸ PRACTICE

for pages 232–233

Problem Solving Strategy: **Make Notes**

Solve each problem. Make notes when it helps.

1. Frank decided to sell some of his old toys and books. He sold 5 books for 25¢ each, 4 Robo Commanders for $1 each, and 3 games for $1.50 each. He also sold an old pogo stick for $3.50. If he spent $5.75 for lunch, how much did he have left? _____ $7.50 _____

2. Connie is designing a new tile floor. She will alternate red and white tiles to make a checkerboard pattern. There will be 9 tiles in each row and 12 rows in all. How many white tiles will Connie need? _____ 54 tiles _____

3. There are 15 girls and 13 boys on the school gymnastics team. They will march into a gymnastics meet in the form of a triangle. In the first row will be 1 team member holding the flag. The 2nd row will have 2 members, the 3rd row 3 members, the 4th row 4 members, and so on. In how many rows will the gymnastic team march into the meet? _____ 7 rows _____

4. Can the gymnastics team have alternate rows of girls and boys? _____ no _____

5. On their birthday, the triplets each received $20 from their parents. Their grandfather gave them $40 to share. Their grandmother gave them $35 to share. Their aunt gave each of them $10. How much did each child receive? _____ $55 _____

6. From their birthday money, the triplets equally shared the cost of a $24 chemistry set. How much did each child have left? _____ $47 _____

7.11 PRACTICE

for pages 234–235

Dividing Money

Divide.

$0.73	$2.84	$2.07
1. 5)$3.65 M	**2.** 6)$17.04 F	**3.** 8)$16.56 O
$3.65	$8.70	$0.41
4. 7)$25.55 S	**5.** 4)$34.80 R	**6.** 9)$3.69 I
$1.89	$3.94	$5.52
7. 3)$5.67 H	**8.** 6)$23.64 B	**9.** 5)$27.60 A
$0.49	$4.21	$7.06
10. 9)$4.41 N	**11.** 4)$16.84 K	**12.** 3)$21.18 C
$7.60	$4.14	$4.06
13. 2)$15.20 U	**14.** 7)$28.98 A	**15.** 6)$24.36 N
$0.51	$7.85	$7.99
16. 3)$1.53 C	**17.** 4)$31.40 T	**18.** 3)$23.97 O

Find the letter beside each quotient above. Write the letter on the line above the correct quotient below to complete the sentence.

Chris withdraws money
 F   R   O   M
$2.84 $8.70 $2.07 $0.73

 H   I   S   B   A   N   K
$1.89 $0.41 $3.65 $3.94 $5.52 $0.49 $4.21

 A   C   C   O   U   N   T
$4.14 $7.06 $0.51 $7.99 $7.60 $4.06 $7.85

7.12 PRACTICE for pages 236–237

Using Division Sense

Estimate. Circle the letter of the correct answer.

1. 168 ÷ 3   (C) 56   O 66   W 76
2. 305 ÷ 5   T 81   (H) 61   E 41
3. 1498 ÷ 7   (I) 214   T 114   S 24
4. 594 ÷ 6   O 89   I 109   (L) 99
5. 1256 ÷ 4   P 414   R 214   (O) 314
6. 520 ÷ 8   K 75   (I) 65   D 55
7. 2092 ÷ 4   B 52   I 73   (G) 523
8. 2943 ÷ 9   (O) 327   R 427   E 527
9. 182 ÷ 7   R 36   (A) 26   M 206
10. 324 ÷ 6   (N) 54   U 64   T 74

Estimate. Circle the letter of the correct symbol.

11. 75 × 10 ● 78 ÷ 10   (L) >   A <   X =
12. 225 ÷ 3 ● 285 ÷ 3   A >   (C) <   E =
13. 0 ÷ 67 ● 67 × 0   W >   A <   (S) =
14. 458 ÷ 8 ● 458 ÷ 7   H >   (I) <   D =
15. 139 ÷ 1 ● 139 × 1   T >   R <   (I) =

Write the letter next to the answer to each exercise above on the matching line below to answer the question.
What city is called the Windy City?

C	H	I	C	A	G	O
12	2	6	1	9	7	5

I	L	L	I	N	O	I	S
14	4	11	3	10	8	15	13

(4) **100**

7.13 ▶ PRACTICE

for pages 238–239

Finding Averages

Find the average. Match the numbers on each scarf with the correct average on a hat. Draw a line from the dot after each scarf to the dot before each hat.

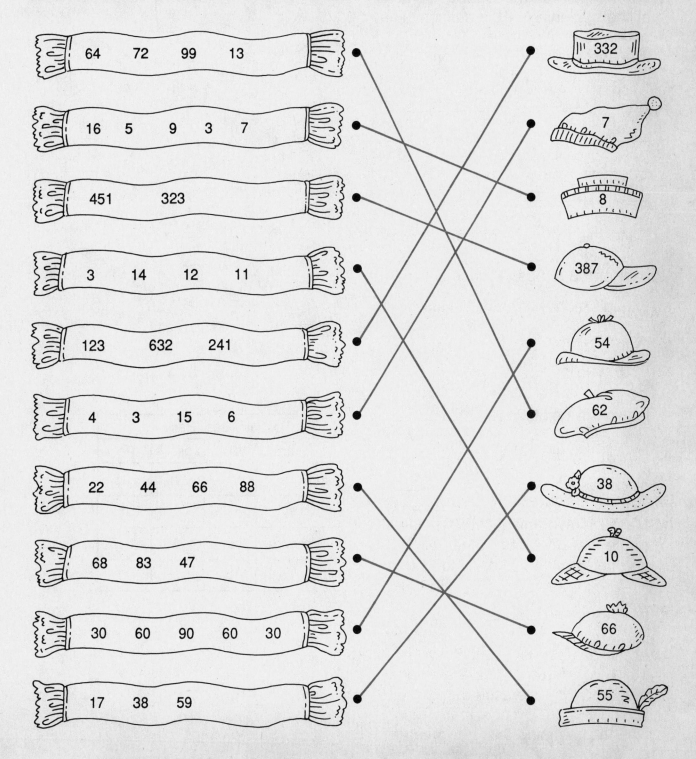

Scarf	Hat
64 72 99 13	332
16 5 9 3 7	7
451 323	8
3 14 12 11	387
123 632 241	54
4 3 15 6	62
22 44 66 88	38
68 83 47	10
30 60 90 60 30	66
17 38 59	55

7.14 ▸ PRACTICE   for page 240

···

Problem Solving: **Using Math Sense**

Solve each problem. Estimate when you can.

1. The softball team bought equipment at the beginning of the season. They bought 6 bats, 8 gloves, and 2 dozen softballs. Did the price of these items total more than $300?

   How do you know? __**Answers may**__ __**vary but may include: yes; the**__ __**gloves and bats cost about $300**__ __**and the softballs cost about $80.**__

gloves $19.98

bat $25

softballs →$4 each or $40 per dozen

shoes $35

base $10.98 $8.75   caps

2. Carol has $75 to spend on equipment. She wants to buy shoes, a glove, a cap, and 3 softballs. Does she have enough money for all the items? __no__

3. In the Softball League, teams receive 3 points for each win and 2 points for each tie. Which team is leading in points? ____**Ardsley**____

4. How many points does the second-place team have? ____**20 points**____

Softball Team Records			
Team	Wins	Losses	Ties
Elmville	6	4	1
Ardsley	7	3	1
Tuckahoe	3	6	2
Sayville	3	6	2

5. Marcia is averaging 4 runs a game. In the first 3 games of the season, she got 6 runs, 2 runs, and 3 runs. How many runs did she get in the fourth game? ____**5 runs**____

6. In the games they won, Sayville scored 15, 17, and 16 runs. In the games they lost, Sayville scored 8, 10, 6, 0, 5, and 7 runs. By how many runs was their winning average greater than their losing average? ____**10 runs**____

PRACTICE

Fractions

Write what fraction of each bar is shaded.

1.
$$\frac{1}{2}$$

2.
$$\frac{3}{4}$$

3.
$$\frac{2}{5}$$

4.
$$\frac{4}{6}$$

5.
$$\frac{3}{10}$$

6.
$$\frac{1}{4}$$

7.
$$\frac{2}{3}$$

8.
$$\frac{5}{8}$$

9.
$$\frac{7}{10}$$

10.
$$\frac{6}{12}$$

11.
$$\frac{4}{5}$$

12.
$$\frac{2}{8}$$

Complete the Fraction Bar for each fraction.

13. $\frac{1}{3}$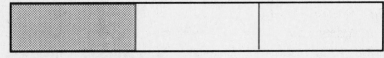

14. $\frac{2}{4}$

15. $\frac{3}{5}$

8.2 ◢ PRACTICE/RECORDING SHEET for pages 250–251

Fractions and Equivalence

8.3 ▶ PRACTICE

for pages 252–253

Equivalence and Simplest Form

Match each Fraction Bar at the left with an equivalent Fraction Bar at the right.

1. ___b___ 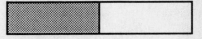 a.

2. ___e___  b.

3. ___h___  c.

4. ___d___ 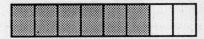 d.

5. ___a___  e.

6. ___g___  f.

7. ___c___  g.

8. ___f___ 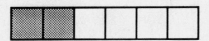 h.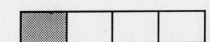

Complete.

9. $\dfrac{3}{4} = \dfrac{\boxed{9}}{12}$

10. $\dfrac{4}{10} = \dfrac{\boxed{2}}{5}$

11. $\dfrac{2}{2} = \dfrac{\boxed{6}}{6}$

12. $\dfrac{6}{8} = \dfrac{\boxed{3}}{4}$

13. $\dfrac{6}{12} = \dfrac{\boxed{1}}{2}$

14. $\dfrac{8}{12} = \dfrac{\boxed{2}}{3}$

8.4 PRACTICE/RECORDING SHEET for pages 254–255

Exploring Order of Fractions

halves

thirds

fourths

fifths

sixths

eighths

tenths

twelfths

8.5 ▸ PRACTICE

Comparing and Ordering Fractions

The fractions in the machines shown below will come out in order from least to greatest.

Write the fractions in the order that they will come out of each machine.

1.
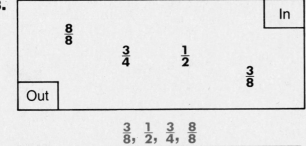

$$\frac{1}{4}, \frac{1}{2}, \frac{3}{4}$$

2.
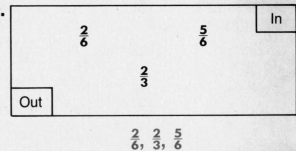

$$\frac{2}{6}, \frac{2}{3}, \frac{5}{6}$$

3.
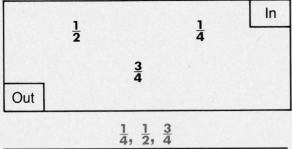

$$\frac{3}{8}, \frac{1}{2}, \frac{3}{4}, \frac{8}{8}$$

4.
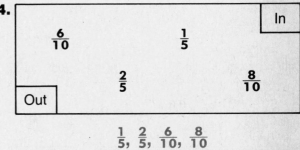

$$\frac{1}{5}, \frac{2}{5}, \frac{6}{10}, \frac{8}{10}$$

5.
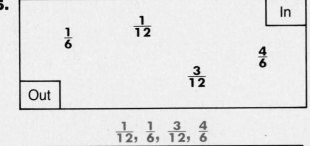

$$\frac{1}{12}, \frac{1}{6}, \frac{3}{12}, \frac{4}{6}$$

6.
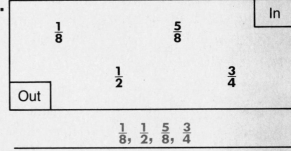

$$\frac{1}{8}, \frac{1}{2}, \frac{5}{8}, \frac{3}{4}$$

7.
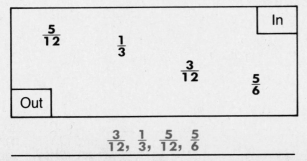

$$\frac{3}{12}, \frac{1}{3}, \frac{5}{12}, \frac{5}{6}$$

8.
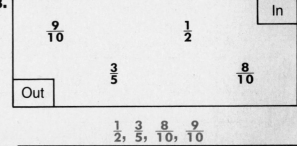

$$\frac{1}{2}, \frac{3}{5}, \frac{8}{10}, \frac{9}{10}$$

8.6 PRACTICE

Problem Solving: Using Math Sense

Read each story. Does the underlined sentence make sense? Tell why or why not.

1. Mrs. Anderson's class went on a picnic. Of her students, $\frac{1}{2}$ are girls and $\frac{1}{4}$ are boys.

   Does not make sense; if $\frac{1}{2}$ are girls, then $\frac{1}{2}$ should be boys.

2. When the boys played tag, Li was "It" for 10 minutes and John was "It" for $\frac{1}{2}$ the time they played.

   makes sense if they played at least 20 minutes

3. The students played softball. In one inning, Jane scored $\frac{1}{3}$ of the runs, Tom scored $\frac{1}{3}$ of the runs, and Jay scored $\frac{1}{3}$ of the runs.

   makes sense

	1	2	3
Team A	0	6	
Team B	0	3	

4. Half of Mrs. Anderson's class was on one team. The other 12 students were on the other team. So, there must be 24 students in her class.

   makes sense

5. Kevin drank $\frac{1}{4}$ cup of his fruit juice. Janice drank $\frac{1}{4}$ of a large carton of juice. "I drank more than you did," said Janice.

   makes sense

6. On the bus ride home, $\frac{3}{4}$ of the students sang for $\frac{1}{4}$ of the time and $\frac{1}{4}$ of the students sang for $\frac{3}{4}$ of the time.

   makes sense

8.7 PRACTICE/RECORDING SHEET for pages 260–261

Exploring Fractional Parts of a Number

1. _____3_____

2. _____$\frac{1}{3}$ or one third_____

3. _____36_____

4. _____12_____

5. _____$\frac{12}{36}$ or $\frac{1}{3}$_____

6. _____12_____

7.

Chart A	
$\frac{1}{2}$ of 24:	12
$\frac{1}{3}$ of 24:	8
$\frac{2}{3}$ of 24:	16
$\frac{1}{4}$ of 24:	6
$\frac{3}{4}$ of 24:	18
$\frac{1}{6}$ of 24:	4
$\frac{1}{8}$ of 24:	3
$\frac{3}{8}$ of 24:	9

9.

Chart B	
$\frac{1}{2}$ of 20:	10
$\frac{1}{4}$ of 20:	5
$\frac{3}{4}$ of 20:	15
$\frac{1}{5}$ of 20:	4
$\frac{2}{5}$ of 20:	8
$\frac{1}{10}$ of 20:	2
$\frac{10}{10}$ of 20:	20

8. Answers may vary: The denominator shows how many equal groups to make.

10. Answers may vary: The denominator shows how many equal groups to make.

11. It tells how many groups to make. _____

12. Answers may vary but may include: divide by 5. _____

13. Answers may vary but may include: find $\frac{1}{5}$ of 25, then multiply by 2.

8.8 PRACTICE

for pages 262–263

Fractional Parts of a Number

Write the answer. Find the answer at the bottom of the page and write its letter on the line above it. What advice is given?

A $\frac{1}{2}$ of 22 ____11____   **B** $\frac{1}{12}$ of 24 ____2____   **C** $\frac{1}{5}$ of 25 ____5____

D $\frac{3}{5}$ of 20 ____12____   **E** $\frac{1}{5}$ of 20 ____4____   **F** $\frac{1}{5}$ of 10 ____2____

G $\frac{1}{4}$ of 8 ____2____   **H** $\frac{1}{3}$ of 21 ____7____   **I** $\frac{2}{3}$ of 21 ____14____

J $\frac{1}{5}$ of 10 ____2____   **K** $\frac{1}{6}$ of 12 ____2____   **L** $\frac{3}{5}$ of 40 ____24____

M $\frac{3}{4}$ of 12 ____9____   **N** $\frac{1}{3}$ of 18 ____6____   **O** $\frac{5}{6}$ of 36 ____30____

P $\frac{1}{2}$ of 10 ____5____   **Q** $\frac{1}{10}$ of 20 ____2____   **R** $\frac{3}{4}$ of 20 ____15____

S $\frac{1}{2}$ of 16 ____8____   **U** $\frac{1}{3}$ of 9 ____3____   **V** $\frac{1}{3}$ of 30 ____10____

W $\frac{4}{5}$ of 35 ____28____   **Y** $\frac{4}{5}$ of 20 ____16____   **Z** $\frac{1}{10}$ of 50 ____5____

Y	O	U		S	H	O	U	L	D
16	30	3		8	7	30	3	24	12

N	E	V	E	R		S	W	I	M
6	4	10	4	15		8	28	14	9

A	L	O	N	E
11	24	30	6	4

PRACTICE

8.9

....

Problem Solving: Using Strategies

Solve each problem. Use one of the strategies you have learned.

1. Wendy is designing a sign for her new restaurant, The Snappy Tomato. The sign will be one foot high and will hang in the window as shown. What fraction of the window will be covered by the sign?

$\frac{1}{8}$

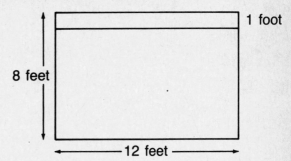

2. The sign will be in 2 colors. The letters will be one color and the background a different color. Wendy likes red, white, and green. How many different combinations of 2 colors can she use? What are they?

3 combinations: red–white, red–green, white–green

3. Wendy wants to put pictures along one wall of the restaurant. Each picture is 24 inches wide and 18 inches high. There will be 12 inches between pictures and 12 inches between the end pictures and the wall. How many pictures can Wendy put on the walls?

6 pictures

────── 228 inches ──────

4. Harvey and Fern are Wendy's first customers. Each of them wants a main dish, a salad, and something to drink. They want to spend no more than $10 each. Can they order different dishes and still spend no more than $10 each? What should each order?

Yes, answers may vary.

The Snappy Tomato

Salads
Green Salad $2.00
Tomato Salad $3.00
Spinach and Bacon $5.00
Main Dishes
Spaghetti........................... $3.00
Chicken............................. $4.00
Steak $6.00
Fish................................ $5.00
Drinks
Mineral Water $2.00
Juice............................... $1.50
Soda................................ $1.00

8.10 ▶ **PRACTICE**

Mixed Numbers

How many bars are shaded? Write your answer as a fraction and as a mixed number.

1.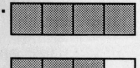

$\frac{7}{4}$, $1\frac{3}{4}$

2.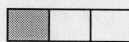

$\frac{10}{3}$, $3\frac{1}{3}$

3.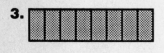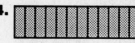

$\frac{21}{8}$, $2\frac{5}{8}$

4.

$\frac{19}{12}$, $1\frac{7}{12}$

5.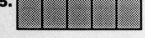

$\frac{16}{5}$, $3\frac{1}{5}$

6.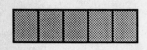

$\frac{5}{2}$, $2\frac{1}{2}$

Write the two whole numbers each mixed number is between.

7. $3\frac{7}{8}$ _____ 3 and 4

8. $11\frac{2}{5}$ _____ 11 and 12

9. $4\frac{3}{8}$ _____ 4 and 5

10. $100\frac{1}{4}$ _____ 100 and 101

11. $79\frac{1}{2}$ _____ 79 and 80

12. $28\frac{2}{3}$ _____ 28 and 29

8.11 ▸ PRACTICE

Problem Solving: Using Strategies

Solve each problem. Use one of the strategies you have learned.

The scoreboard below shows the results of a Little League baseball game between the Bears and the Tigers.

Inning

	1	2	3	4	5	6	Runs
Bears	3	0	3	6	1	4	17
Tigers	2	2	4	0	6	2	16

1. Which team scored half its runs in the first three innings? How do you know? _____ **Tigers; 8 is $\frac{1}{2}$ of 16** _____

2. What was the score after half the game had been played? _____ **Tigers 8, Bears 6** _____

3. In which inning did one team score half as many points as the other team? _____ **6th inning** _____

4. Which team was leading after two-thirds of the game had been played? By how many runs? _____ **The Bears were** _____ **leading by 4 runs.** _____

5. How many runs did the Bears score in five-sixths of the game? _____ **13 runs** _____

6. The game began at 2:15 P.M. and ended at 4:30 P.M. How many hours did the game last? _____ **$2\frac{1}{4}$ hours** _____

7. When Mary opened the refreshment stand, she had 6 packages of lemonade to sell. Each package contained 6 cans of lemonade. She sold three quarters of the cans during the game. How many cans of lemonade did Mary sell? _____ **27 cans of lemonade** _____

9.1 PRACTICE for pages 276–277

Adding and Subtracting Like Fractions

Write the answer in the box.

1. $\frac{3}{5} + \frac{1}{5} =$ $\boxed{\frac{4}{5} \quad A}$

2. $\frac{9}{10} - \frac{6}{10} =$ $\boxed{\frac{3}{10} \quad O}$

3. $\frac{7}{8} - \frac{2}{8} =$ $\boxed{\frac{5}{8} \quad P}$

4. $\frac{5}{8} - \frac{2}{8} =$ $\boxed{\frac{3}{8} \quad S}$

5. $\frac{2}{5} + \frac{1}{5} =$ $\boxed{\frac{3}{5} \quad E}$

6. $\frac{4}{8} + \frac{3}{8} =$ $\boxed{\frac{7}{8} \quad D}$

7. $\frac{3}{10} - \frac{2}{10} =$ $\boxed{\frac{1}{10} \quad I}$

8. $\frac{3}{12} + \frac{4}{12} =$ $\boxed{\frac{7}{12} \quad G}$

9. $\frac{7}{8} - \frac{6}{8} =$ $\boxed{\frac{1}{8} \quad M}$

10. $\frac{8}{12} + \frac{3}{12} =$ $\boxed{\frac{11}{12} \quad Y}$

11. $\frac{4}{12} + \frac{7}{12} =$ $\boxed{\frac{11}{12} \quad Y}$

12. $\frac{9}{10} - \frac{8}{10} =$ $\boxed{\frac{1}{10} \quad I}$

13. $\frac{5}{6} - \frac{4}{6} =$ $\boxed{\frac{1}{6} \quad T}$

14. $\frac{4}{5} - \frac{1}{5} =$ $\boxed{\frac{3}{5} \quad E}$

15. $\frac{2}{6} + \frac{3}{6} =$ $\boxed{\frac{5}{6} \quad F}$

16. $\frac{2}{4} + \frac{1}{4} =$ $\boxed{\frac{3}{4} \quad R}$

17. $\frac{6}{12} + \frac{5}{12} =$ $\boxed{\frac{11}{12} \quad Y}$

18. $\frac{3}{6} - \frac{2}{6} =$ $\boxed{\frac{1}{6} \quad T}$

19. $\frac{9}{12} - \frac{2}{12} =$ $\boxed{\frac{7}{12} \quad G}$

20. $\frac{5}{8} - \frac{4}{8} =$ $\boxed{\frac{1}{8} \quad M}$

21. $\frac{5}{8} + \frac{2}{8} =$ $\boxed{\frac{7}{8} \quad D}$

22. $\frac{8}{10} - \frac{7}{10} =$ $\boxed{\frac{1}{10} \quad I}$

23. $\frac{5}{12} + \frac{6}{12} =$ $\boxed{\frac{11}{12} \quad Y}$

24. $\frac{7}{8} - \frac{2}{8} =$ $\boxed{\frac{5}{8} \quad P}$

Find the answer you wrote in each box under one of the lines below. Write the letter from the box on the line. The letters will spell the answer to the riddle.

What is the name of one of the Seven Wonders of the World?

P	Y	R	A	M	I	D	S	O	F	E	G	Y	P	T
$\frac{5}{8}$	$\frac{11}{12}$	$\frac{3}{4}$	$\frac{4}{5}$	$\frac{1}{8}$	$\frac{1}{10}$	$\frac{7}{8}$	$\frac{3}{8}$	$\frac{3}{10}$	$\frac{5}{6}$	$\frac{3}{5}$	$\frac{7}{12}$	$\frac{11}{12}$	$\frac{5}{8}$	$\frac{1}{6}$

9.2 PRACTICE

Using Fractions

Use the pictures to solve each problem.

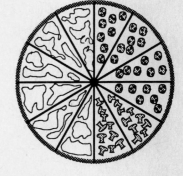

1. About what fraction of the pizza has pepperoni?

about $\frac{4}{12}$, $\frac{2}{6}$, or $\frac{1}{3}$

_____

2. About what fraction of the pizza has mushrooms?

about $\frac{2}{12}$, or $\frac{1}{6}$

_____

3. About what fraction of the pizza has cheese only?

about $\frac{6}{12}$, $\frac{3}{6}$, or $\frac{1}{2}$

_____

4. About what fraction of the pizza has no pepperoni?

about $\frac{8}{12}$, $\frac{4}{6}$, or $\frac{2}{3}$

_____

5. About what fraction of the pizza has no mushrooms?

about $\frac{10}{12}$, or $\frac{5}{6}$

_____

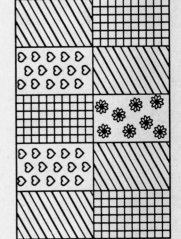

6. About what fraction of the quilt has a flower design?

about $\frac{1}{10}$

_____

7. About what fraction of the quilt has a heart design?

about $\frac{2}{10}$, or $\frac{1}{5}$

_____

8. About what fraction of the quilt has a checkered design?

about $\frac{3}{10}$

_____

9. About what fraction of the quilt has a striped design?

about $\frac{4}{10}$, or $\frac{2}{5}$

_____

9.3 PRACTICE

for pages 280–281

Adding and Subtracting Fractions

Use Fraction Bars to add.

1. $\dfrac{1}{2} + \dfrac{1}{4} = \underline{\dfrac{3}{4}}$
2. $\dfrac{3}{8} + \dfrac{1}{4} = \underline{\dfrac{5}{8}}$
3. $\dfrac{1}{3} + \dfrac{1}{6} = \underline{\dfrac{3}{6}}$
4. $\dfrac{1}{8} + \dfrac{3}{4} = \underline{\dfrac{7}{8}}$

5. $\dfrac{5}{12} + \dfrac{2}{6} = \underline{\dfrac{9}{12}}$
6. $\dfrac{3}{10} + \dfrac{2}{5} = \underline{\dfrac{7}{10}}$
7. $\dfrac{1}{2} + \dfrac{3}{6} = \underline{\dfrac{6}{6} \text{ or } 1}$
8. $\dfrac{1}{2} + \dfrac{1}{8} = \underline{\dfrac{5}{8}}$

9. $\dfrac{5}{6} + \dfrac{1}{12} = \underline{\dfrac{11}{12}}$
10. $\dfrac{1}{4} + \dfrac{1}{8} = \underline{\dfrac{3}{8}}$
11. $\dfrac{1}{6} + \dfrac{2}{3} = \underline{\dfrac{5}{6}}$
12. $\dfrac{2}{6} + \dfrac{3}{12} = \underline{\dfrac{7}{12}}$

13. $\dfrac{4}{6} + \dfrac{2}{12} = \underline{\dfrac{10}{12}}$
14. $\dfrac{2}{6} + \dfrac{1}{2} = \underline{\dfrac{5}{6}}$
15. $\dfrac{3}{4} + \dfrac{2}{8} = \underline{\dfrac{8}{8} \text{ or } 1}$
16. $\dfrac{7}{12} + \dfrac{2}{6} = \underline{\dfrac{11}{12}}$

Use Fraction Bars to subtract.

17. $\dfrac{3}{4} - \dfrac{2}{8} = \underline{\dfrac{4}{8}}$
18. $\dfrac{1}{2} - \dfrac{1}{6} = \underline{\dfrac{2}{6}}$
19. $\dfrac{5}{8} - \dfrac{1}{4} = \underline{\dfrac{3}{8}}$
20. $\dfrac{1}{4} - \dfrac{1}{8} = \underline{\dfrac{1}{8}}$

21. $\dfrac{11}{12} - \dfrac{1}{2} = \underline{\dfrac{5}{12}}$
22. $\dfrac{5}{6} - \dfrac{2}{3} = \underline{\dfrac{1}{6}}$
23. $\dfrac{2}{3} - \dfrac{2}{6} = \underline{\dfrac{2}{6}}$
24. $\dfrac{1}{2} - \dfrac{4}{8} = \underline{\dfrac{0}{8} \text{ or } 0}$

25. $\dfrac{6}{8} - \dfrac{1}{2} = \underline{\dfrac{2}{8}}$
26. $\dfrac{3}{4} - \dfrac{1}{2} = \underline{\dfrac{1}{4}}$
27. $\dfrac{3}{6} - \dfrac{2}{12} = \underline{\dfrac{4}{12}}$
28. $\dfrac{9}{10} - \dfrac{1}{5} = \underline{\dfrac{7}{10}}$

29. $\dfrac{4}{6} - \dfrac{1}{2} = \underline{\dfrac{1}{6}}$
30. $\dfrac{5}{6} - \dfrac{3}{12} = \underline{\dfrac{7}{12}}$
31. $\dfrac{1}{3} - \dfrac{1}{6} = \underline{\dfrac{1}{6}}$
32. $\dfrac{11}{12} - \dfrac{5}{12} = \underline{\dfrac{6}{12}}$

9.4 PRACTICE

Choose a Computation Method

The fourth-grade students at the Willow
Middle School are going to the Caves
and Minerals Museum.

Solve each problem. Tell which computation method you used.

Solution methods may vary.

1. The 105 fourth-grade students will be going by bus.
   Each bus seat holds 2 students. If students are paired,
   how many students will not be sitting with another student?

   1 student
   _____

2. Sixty-nine of the students will be taking the cave tour in
   the morning. Tour guides will lead groups of 5 students.
   How many students will be in a group that has fewer

   than 5 students? _____ **4 students** _____

3. Seventy-eight of the students will examine the rock and
   mineral pile before lunch. The students will look for minerals in groups of 3. How many groups of 3 will there
   be?

   26 groups
   _____

4. The students will collect 105 rock and mineral samples
   and pack them in boxes. Each box will hold 9 samples.
   How many boxes will be needed in all?

   12 boxes
   _____

5. At lunch, all 105 students will eat at picnic tables. Each
   picnic table seats 8 students. How many picnic tables
   will be needed in all?

   14 tables
   _____

6. Mr. Jade will bring 11 watermelons for the picnic. Into
   how many pieces will he need to cut each watermelon
   so that each of the 105 students will get the largest
   piece possible?

   10 pieces
   _____

9.5 PRACTICE

for pages 284–285

Adding Unlike Fractions

Add down and across. Write the sum in the circle. Use your Fraction Bars when it helps. Write the sum in simplest form.

1.

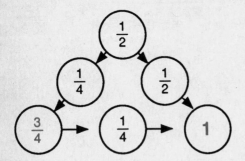

2.

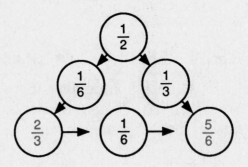

3.

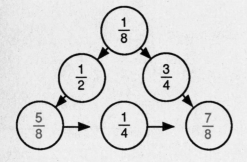

4.

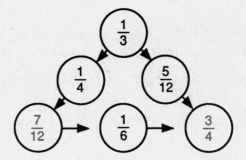

5.

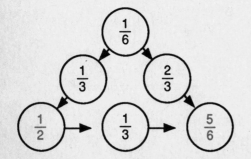

6.

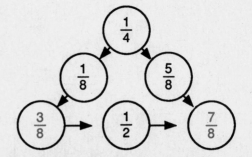

Subtracting Unlike Fractions

Subtract the fraction in the center from each fraction in the inner circle. Write the difference in simplest form in the outer circle. Use Fraction Bars when it helps.

1.
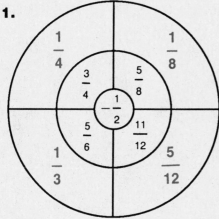

2.
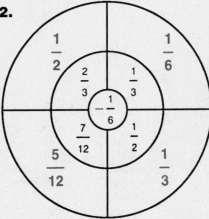

3.
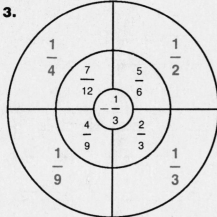

4.
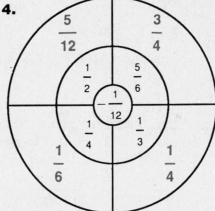

5.
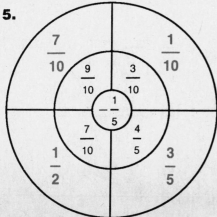

6.
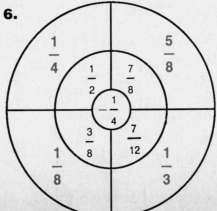

9.7 PRACTICE

for pages 288–289

Adding and Subtracting Mixed Numbers

Write each answer in simplest form.

1. $1\frac{4}{8}$
$+\ 2\frac{1}{8}$
___
$3\frac{5}{8}$

2. $2\frac{1}{4}$
$+\ 3\frac{2}{4}$
___
$5\frac{3}{4}$

3. $6\frac{3}{4}$
$-\ 1\frac{2}{4}$
___
$5\frac{1}{4}$

4. $3\frac{5}{8}$
$-\ 1\frac{2}{8}$
___
$2\frac{3}{8}$

5. $2\frac{1}{8}$
$+\ 1\frac{2}{8}$
___
$3\frac{3}{8}$

6. $2\frac{1}{6}$
$+\ 1\frac{2}{6}$
___
$3\frac{1}{2}$

7. $5\frac{9}{10}$
$-\ 2\frac{2}{10}$
___
$3\frac{7}{10}$

8. $7\frac{1}{8}$
$+\ 2\frac{2}{8}$
___
$9\frac{3}{8}$

9. $4\frac{5}{6}$
$-\ 1\frac{4}{6}$
___
$3\frac{1}{6}$

10. $5\frac{2}{6}$
$+\ 2\frac{1}{6}$
___
$7\frac{1}{2}$

11. $7\frac{1}{8}$
$+\ 1\frac{2}{8}$
___
$8\frac{3}{8}$

12. $6\frac{7}{8}$
$-\ 2\frac{2}{8}$
___
$4\frac{5}{8}$

13. $4\frac{9}{10}$
$-\ 1\frac{5}{10}$
___
$3\frac{2}{5}$

14. $3\frac{1}{5}$
$+\ 3\frac{3}{5}$
___
$6\frac{4}{5}$

15. $6\frac{11}{12}$
$-\ 4\frac{4}{12}$
___
$2\frac{7}{12}$

16. $5\frac{1}{12}$
$+\ 3\frac{6}{12}$
___
$8\frac{7}{12}$

17. $8\frac{7}{12}$
$+\ 3\frac{3}{12}$
___
$11\frac{5}{6}$

18. $4\frac{9}{10}$
$-\ 2\frac{2}{10}$
___
$2\frac{7}{10}$

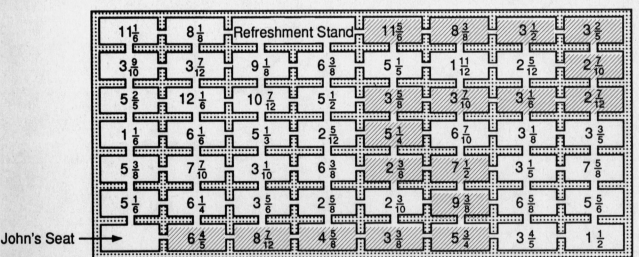

John wants to go to the refreshment stand. To do so, he has to find his way through the seats of the stadium.

Shade the seats that contain the answers above to help John find his way to the stand.

(4) **120**

Name ______________________ Date ______________

9.8 PRACTICE

pages 290–291

Problem Solving Strategy: Use Simpler Numbers

Solve each problem. Use simpler numbers when it helps.

1. Mrs. Alvarez bought 4 bags of groceries. All the bags weigh $26\frac{7}{8}$ pounds. The first bag weighs $7\frac{1}{8}$ pounds, the second weighs $6\frac{3}{8}$ pounds, and the third weighs $8\frac{1}{8}$ pounds. How much does the fourth bag weigh?

	Actual Numbers	Simpler Numbers
Total Weight	$26\frac{7}{8}$ →	26
Bag #1	$7\frac{1}{8}$ →	7
Bag #2	$6\frac{3}{8}$ →	6
Bag #3	$8\frac{1}{8}$ →	8

$5\frac{2}{8}$ (or $5\frac{1}{4}$) pounds

2. Denise bought bananas for $2.45 and a watermelon for $1.19. She paid with a $5 bill. How much change did she receive?

	Actual Numbers	Simpler Numbers
bananas	$2.45 →	$2
watermelon	$1.19 →	$1

$1.36

3. Sandy has $1\frac{1}{4}$ cups of beaten eggs. She adds $2\frac{1}{4}$ cups of milk. She then adds enough pancake flour to make $8\frac{3}{4}$ cups of batter. How much pancake flour does she add?

	Actual Numbers	Simpler Numbers
eggs	$1\frac{1}{4}$ →	1
milk	$2\frac{1}{4}$ →	2
Total	$8\frac{3}{4}$ →	8

$5\frac{1}{4}$ cups

4. Tommy and 3 friends each chipped in $5.25 for lunch. The food plus the tip came to $16.84. How much money should each person get back?

	Actual Numbers	Simpler Numbers
Each share	$ 5.25 →	$ 5
Total cost	$16.84 →	$16

$1.04

5. José bought a gallon of milk and 3 dozen eggs. He spent $8.62 in all. The eggs cost $1.89 a dozen. How much did the milk cost?

$2.95

◢ 9.9 ◣ PRACTICE for pages 292–293

Problem Solving Strategy: **Use Simpler Numbers**

Solve each problem. Use simpler numbers or other strategies you think will help you.

1. Lorraine is making dresses for her twin sisters. She has a piece of fabric that is $5\frac{7}{8}$ yards long. Lorraine needs $2\frac{3}{8}$ yards of fabric for each dress. How much fabric will she have left over? _____ $1\frac{1}{8}$ **yards** _____

2. Jim, Dan, and Lou were trading baseball cards. Jim had 32 cards and Dan had 13 cards. The remaining $\frac{1}{2}$ of the cards belonged to Lou. How many baseball cards did Lou have?
45 baseball cards

3. Kevin needs batteries for his cassette player. Batteries cost 89¢ each, or 4 for $3.25. Kevin wants to buy 6 batteries. How much will they cost him? _____ **$5.03** _____

4. Penny and Fran have lunch together. The bill comes to $7.35. The tip is $1.65. The girls decide to split the bill. If each puts in $5.00, how much change should each get back? _____ **50¢** _____

5. Fred's house is $1\frac{1}{4}$ mile from the library. Joyce's house is $1\frac{3}{8}$ mile from the library. Who lives closer to the library? How much closer? _____ **Fred, $\frac{1}{8}$ mile closer** _____

6. Tom wants to make 12 pounds of trail mix. The trail mix will contain $\frac{1}{4}$ raisins, $\frac{1}{2}$ nuts, and $\frac{1}{4}$ dried pineapple. How many pounds of dried pineapple will Tom need? _____ **3 pounds** _____

9.10 PRACTICE

Special Topic: Time Zones

Fill in the chart to show the corresponding times in each pair of cities. Use the time zone map to help you. The first one has been done for you.

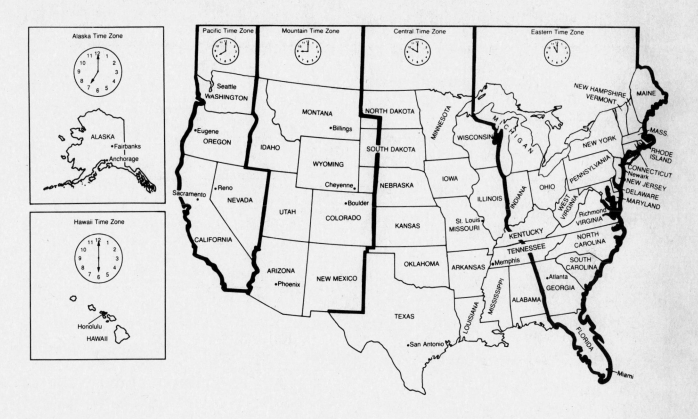

	CITY	TIME	CITY	TIME
1.	Richmond, Virginia	8:00 A.M.	Memphis, Tennessee	7:00 A.M.
2.	Cheyenne, Wyoming	4:00 P.M.	Seattle, Washington	3:00 P.M.
3.	Miami, Florida	3:00 P.M.	Honolulu, Hawaii	10:00 A.M.
4.	Fairbanks, Alaska	1:00 P.M.	Billings, Montana	3:00 P.M.
5.	Newark, New Jersey	11:00 A.M.	Sacramento, California	8:00 A.M.
6.	St. Louis, Missouri	5:00 A.M.	Anchorage, Alaska	2:00 A.M.
7.	Phoenix, Arizona	7:00 P.M.	Reno, Nevada	6:00 P.M.
8.	San Antonio, Texas	12:00 noon	Eugene, Oregon	10:00 A.M.
9.	Atlanta, Georgia	2:00 A.M.	Boulder, Colorado	12:00 midnight

10.1 ▸ PRACTICE   for pages 302–303

Inch, Half Inch, and Quarter Inch

Measure the length to the nearest inch, half inch, and quarter inch.

1.
_____

1 in., 1 in., $1\frac{1}{4}$ in.
_____

2.
_____

3 in., 3 in., 3 in.
_____

3.
_____

2 in., $1\frac{1}{2}$ in., $1\frac{3}{4}$ in.
_____

4.
_____

2 in., 2 in., 2 in.
_____

5.

1 in., $\frac{1}{2}$ in., $\frac{3}{4}$ in.
_____

6.

2 in., $2\frac{1}{2}$ in., $2\frac{1}{2}$ in.
_____

Draw line segments of the following lengths. Use a ruler.

7. $5\frac{1}{4}$ inches

8. $2\frac{1}{2}$ inches

9. 8 inches

10.2 ► PRACTICE

for pages 304–305

Foot, Yard, and Mile

Choose the unit you would use to measure. Write foot, yard, or mile for the unit you would use.

1. You are taking a trip from Montana to Idaho. _____mile_____

2. A wooden beam must be cut for the ceiling of a house. _foot or yard_

3. Someone is marking the lines on a football field. ___foot or yard___

4. You are finding the length and width of your room in order to buy new rugs.
_____foot or yard_____

5. An astronaut wants to know the distance to the space lab from his house.
_____mile_____

6. You want to know the distance from New York City to Los Angeles.
_____mile_____

7. A gardener wants to know the height of a tree. ___foot or yard___

8. A jogger wants to know the length of a track. ___foot or yard___

Complete each table.

1 ft = 12 in.

9.

ft	1	2	3	4
in.	12	24	36	48

10.

in.	24	36	48	60
ft	2	3	4	5

Write the letter of the equivalent measure.

11. 86 inches   d   a. 91 inches

12. 6 feet 3 inches   b   b. 75 inches

13. 63 inches   c   c. 5 feet 3 inches

14. $4\frac{1}{2}$ feet   e   d. 7 feet 2 inches

15. 7 feet 7 inches   a   e. 54 inches

Perimeter

Measure the sides of each figure to the nearest quarter inch.
Write the perimeter.

1. _____ 8 inches _____

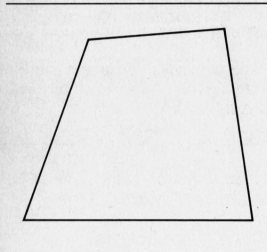

2. _____ 10 inches _____

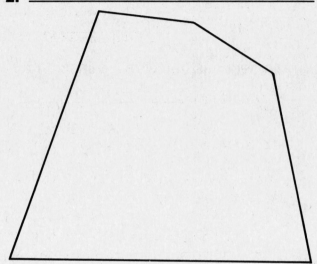

3. _____ 7 inches _____

4. _____ 9 inches _____

5. _____ 12 inches _____

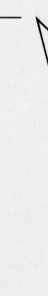

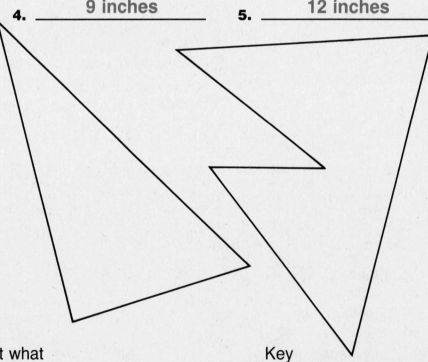

Use your answers to find out what
George's plans are for Saturday.

A   H I K E
1   2 3 4 5

Key

8	7	12	9	10
A	I	E	K	H

10.4 ► PRACTICE/RECORDING SHEET for pages 308–309

Measurement Lab

Answers may vary.

Item	12-inch ruler	Yardstick
1. Height of door		
Perimeter of desktop		
Width of window		
2.		

3. _____

_____

Item	Estimate	Actual Measure	Ruler Used
4.			

5. Answers may vary but may include: 12-inch ruler for small items,
yardstick for larger items.

6. in inches, or feet and inches

_____

7. Answers may vary: feet or yards.

_____

10.5 ◢ PRACTICE

Problem Solving: **Using Strategies**

Solve each problem. Use one of the strategies you have learned.

3 ft = 1 yd	5280 ft = 1 mi	1760 yd = 1 mi	176 yd = $\frac{1}{10}$ mi

1. A jogging track is being planned for a city park. This diagram shows the park.

a. What is the perimeter of the park in miles? _____ $2\frac{8}{10}$ mi or $2\frac{4}{5}$ mi _____

b. How many yards is each long side of the park? _____ **1936 yd** _____

c. How many yards long is each short side of the park? _____ **528 yd** _____

The Park

$\frac{3}{10}$ mile

$1\frac{1}{10}$ miles

2. The designer wants the jogging track to be a 2-mile oval. Will this oval fit in the park?

_____ **yes** _____

The Track

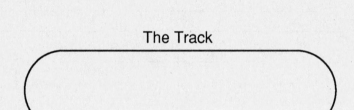

3. The designer wants to make each straight section as long as possible. Should each straight section be 500 yd long, 1000 yd long, 1500 yd long, or 2000 yd long? Why? _____ **1500 yd long; it is the greatest length that will fit into the park.** _____

4. Each curved section is 260 yd long.

a. Is this more than or less than $\frac{1}{2}$ mile? _____ **less than** _____

b. How many feet are there in 260 yd? _____ **780 ft** _____

5. One jogger jogs 440 yd in 3 minutes. If she continues to jog at this speed, how long will it take her to run 1 mile?

_____ **12 minutes** _____

10.6 ▷ PRACTICE

for pages 312–313

Customary Units of Capacity

Make each statement true. Write <, > or =.

Equivalent Units

2 cups	=	1 pint
2 pints	=	1 quart
4 quarts	=	1 gallon

1. 4 quarts $<$ 9 pints
2. 7 gallons $>$ 7 quarts
3. 20 cups $>$ 8 pints
4. 12 pints $>$ 12 cups
5. 5 gallons $=$ 20 quarts
6. 9 cups $<$ 6 pints
7. 6 pints $>$ 11 cups
8. 8 quarts $>$ 4 pints
9. 12 pints $<$ 24 quarts
10. 13 quarts $<$ 5 gallons
11. 8 quarts $<$ 3 gallons
12. 22 pints $=$ 11 quarts
13. 4 cups $<$ 4 pints
14. 6 gallons $=$ 24 quarts
15. 2 gallons $>$ 7 quarts
16. 5 cups $>$ 2 pints
17. 16 quarts $>$ 8 pints
18. 9 pints $<$ 5 quarts
19. 3 pints $<$ 9 cups
20. 13 quarts $<$ 4 gallons
21. 10 quarts $<$ 3 gallons
22. 7 pints $>$ 3 cups
23. 7 cups $>$ 2 pints
24. 8 gallons $=$ 32 quarts
25. 4 gallons $<$ 18 quarts
26. 15 cups $<$ 10 pints
27. 5 pints $=$ 10 cups
28. 7 quarts $>$ 10 pints
29. 16 pints $>$ 4 quarts
30. 20 quarts $=$ 5 gallons
31. 8 quarts $=$ 2 gallons
32. 3 pints $<$ 9 cups

Complete. Make a table or use mental math.

33. 14 c = _____7_____ pt
34. _____16_____ qt = 4 gal
35. 8 qt = _____16_____ pt
36. 9 gal = _____36_____ qt
37. _____8_____ pt = 4 qt
38. _____10_____ pt = 20 c
39. _____16_____ qt = 4 gal
40. 18 c = _____9_____ pt
41. 20 pt = _____10_____ qt
42. _____16_____ pt = 32 c
43. _____40_____ qt = 10 gal
44. 15 gal = _____60_____ qt

10.7 PRACTICE

for page 314

Ounce, Pound, and Ton

Choose the unit you would use to weigh each object. Write oz, lb, or t.

Equivalent Units
1 lb = 16 oz
1 t = 2000 lb

1.

lb

2.

oz

3.

t

4.

lb

5.

t

6.

lb

7.

oz

8.

lb

9.

oz

10.

lb

11.

t

12.

oz or lb

Complete. Write >, <, or =. Make a table when it helps.

13. 3 lb ⊖> 20 oz   **14.** 7 t <⊖ 29,800 lb   **15.** 5 lb <⊖ 85 oz

16. 10,000 lb =⊖ 5 t   **17.** 75 oz >⊖ 4 lb   **18.** 6 lb =⊖ 96 oz

10.8 ▷ PRACTICE

Centimeter and Millimeter

Complete the table. Use a centimeter ruler.

Picture	Measure to the nearest mm	Measure to the nearest cm
1.	50 mm	5 cm
2.	38 mm	4 cm
3.	71 mm	7 cm
4.	67 mm	7 cm
5.	80 mm	8 cm
6.	73 mm	7 cm
7.	24 mm	2 cm

Draw a line segment for each measure.

8. 11 cm

9. 27 mm

10. 3 cm

11. 54 mm

10.9 PRACTICE

for pages 318–319

Decimeter, Meter, and Kilometer

Complete each statement. Make a table or use mental math. Cross out the answer and its letter in the box at the right. The letters that have not been crossed out will answer the riddle below.

Equivalent Units	
1 cm = 10 mm 1 m = 10 dm 1 km = 1000 m	
1 dm = 10 cm 1 m = 100 cm	

4 m = **40** dm   500 cm = **50** dm

200 cm = **2** m   50 km = **50,000** m

6 m = **60** dm   25 m = **250** dm

600 mm = **60** cm   7000 cm = **70** m

70 dm = **7** m   150 mm = **15** cm

8 dm = **80** cm   74 km = **74,000** m

8 km = **8000** m   460 m = **4600** dm

37 cm = **370** mm   90,000 m = **90** km

10 m = **100** dm   290 cm = **2900** mm

4000 m = **4** km   660 cm = **66** dm

400 dm = **40** m   5000 dm = **500** m

85 km = **85,000** m   358 dm = **3580** cm

900 cm = **9** m   100 km = **100,000** m

20 cm = **2** dm   1000 m = **10,000** dm

43,000 m = **43** km   720 mm = **72** cm

80 cm = **8** dm   720 dm = **7200** cm

Answer Key

~~100 dm~~	~~L~~	~~43 km~~	~~Z~~
~~15 cm~~	~~V~~	~~500 m~~	~~Y~~
18 mm	S	~~50,000 m~~	~~P~~
~~10,000 dm~~	~~A~~	~~60 cm~~	~~K~~
~~100,000 m~~	~~N~~	~~60 dm~~	~~D~~
2 cm	W	61 km	I
~~2 m~~	~~E~~	~~66 dm~~	~~O~~
2 km	I	68 m	N
~~2 dm~~	~~F~~	~~7 m~~	~~A~~
~~250 dm~~	~~T~~	~~70 m~~	~~H~~
~~2900 mm~~	~~R~~	~~72 cm~~	~~E~~
~~370 mm~~	~~O~~	~~7200 cm~~	~~R~~
~~3580 cm~~	~~X~~	~~74,000 m~~	~~L~~
~~4 km~~	~~B~~	~~8 dm~~	~~W~~
4 cm	M	80 km	G
~~40 dm~~	~~A~~	~~80 cm~~	~~S~~
~~40 m~~	~~Q~~	~~8000 m~~	~~O~~
~~50 dm~~	~~Z~~	~~85,000 m~~	~~J~~
45 m	M	~~9 m~~	~~F~~
~~4600 dm~~	~~U~~	~~90 km~~	~~E~~

Where do elephants go when they pack their trunks?

__S__ __W__ __I__ __M__ __M__ __I__ __N__ __G__

10.10 PRACTICE   for pages 320–321

Metric Units of Capacity

Compare. Make a table or use mental math. Write >, <, or =. | 1L = 1000 mL

1. 40 mL $<$ 6 L

>	<	=
G	N	L

2. 3000 mL $>$ 2 L

>	<	=
A	B	K

3. 4 L $>$ 500 ml

>	<	=
T	A	C

4. 75,000 mL $>$ 6 L

>	<	=
U	N	A

5. 10,000 mL $<$ 14 L

>	<	=
J	R	M

6. 6000 mL $=$ 6 L

>	<	=
P	Z	A

7. 400 mL $<$ 4 L

>	<	=
Y	L	Q

8. 8,400 mL $>$ 8 L

>	<	=
H	X	I

9. 8000 mL $=$ 8 L

>	<	=
F	W	I

10. 1 L $>$ 70 mL

>	<	=
S	R	D

11. 7 L $>$ 6900 mL

>	<	=
T	B	V

12. 320 mL $<$ 8 L

>	<	=
U	O	C

13. 1000 mL $=$ 1 L

>	<	=
H	S	R

14. 5 L $<$ 79,000 mL

>	<	=
T	Y	E

Use the code letter for each answer to complete the sentence.
Write the letters in the order of the exercises.

You can see fossils and dinosaurs at the Museum of

N	A	T	U	R	A	L	H	I	S	T	O	R	Y
1	2	3	4	5	6	7	8	9	10	11	12	13	14

Name _____ Date _____

10.11 PRACTICE for page 322

Gram and Kilogram

Circle the best estimate.

 = 1 g    = 1 kg

1.

(5 g)   5 kg   8 kg

2.

5 g   115 g   (2 kg)

3.

18 g   7 kg   (600 kg)

4.

4 g   (4 kg)   140 kg

5.

2 g   10 g   (1200 g)

6.

(8 g)   85 g   850 g

7.

8 g   (8 kg)   800 kg

8.

(35 g)   1 kg   3 kg

9.

1g   (15 g)   4 kg

10.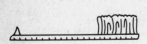

(4 g)   85 g   5 kg

11.

15 g   (375 g)   15 kg

12.

(900 g)   8 kg   80 kg

13.

7 g   (104 g)   230 g

14.

(55 g)   3 kg   13 kg

15.

6 g   (1500 g)   150 kg

16.

5 g   (500 g)   5 kg

17.

60 g   (6 kg)   600 kg

18.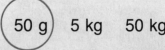

(50 g)   5 kg   50 kg

© D.C. Heath and Company

(4) 134

10.12 ▸ PRACTICE   for page 323

Problem Solving: **Using Strategies**

Solve each problem. Use strategies you have learned.

1. The school wants to put a new fence around the children's playground. The playground is 24 meters long and 20 meters wide.

   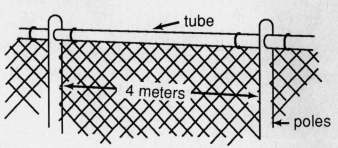

   a. How many meters of fencing will be needed? _____**88 meters**_____

   b. Poles to hold up the fencing will be placed every 4 meters. How many poles will be needed?

   _____**22 poles**_____

   c. The iron tube at the top of the fence comes in sections 2 meters long. How many sections will be needed for the entire fence?

   _____**44 sections**_____

2. The junior high's schoolyard is the same length as the children's play-ground, but it is twice as wide. How many iron tubes will be needed for the fence around this schoolyard?

   _____**64 iron tubes**_____

3. A garden 3 meters wide is planned all along one 24-meter side of the junior high's schoolyard.

   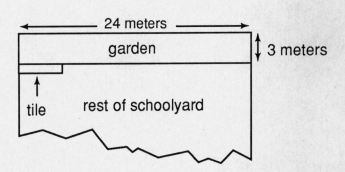

   a. What will be the perimeter of the garden?

   _____**54 meters**_____

   b. Slate tiles will make up the border of the garden. Each tile is 3 meters long. How many tiles will be needed for the entire border?

   _____**18 tiles**_____

10.13 ▷ PRACTICE   for pages 324–325

Temperature

Circle the letter of the best temperature for each activity.

1. A picnic in the park

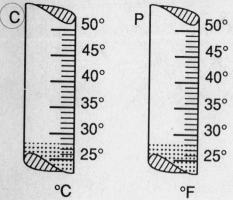

2. A sleigh ride

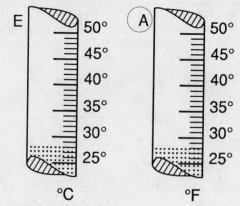

3. Outdoor tennis

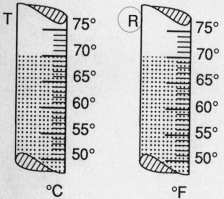

4. Raking leaves

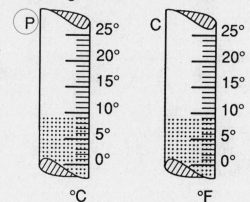

5. Ice Skating

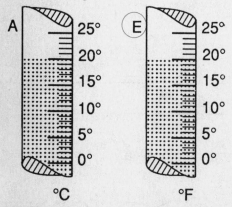

6. Going to the beach

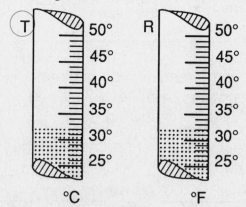

Write the letter you circled for each answer to solve the riddle.

What kind of pet is always found in an automobile?

A   C   A   R   P   E   T
___ ___ ___ ___ ___ ___ ___
     1   2   3   4   5   6

10.14 PRACTICE

Elapsed Time

Mr. McCarthy will spend three weeks traveling by train in the United States. He wrote out a schedule. Help him find how long each trip will take.

1 min	=	60 s
1 h	=	60 min
1 day	=	24 h

Write the elapsed time.

Leave		Arrive		Trip Time
New York City	5:00 P.M.	Philadelphia	6:11 P.M.	1 h 11 min
Philadelphia	10:10 A.M.	Baltimore	11:13 A.M.	1 h 3 min
Baltimore	7:14 A.M.	Washington	7:49 A.M.	35 min
Washington	5:40 P.M.	Richmond	8:00 P.M.	2 h 20 min
Richmond	3:46 P.M.	Charleston	10:10 P.M.	6 h 24 min
Charleston	8:15 P.M.	Washington	6:00 A.M.	9 h 45 min
Washington	6:30 P.M.	Miami	6:50 P.M. (next day)	24 h 20 min
Miami	1:40 P.M.	Savannah	9:32 P.M.	7 h 52 min
Savannah	12:48 A.M.	Louisville	8:14 A.M.	7 h 26 min
Louisville	6:01 P.M.	Toledo	12:05 A.M.	6 h 4 min
Toledo	9:44 P.M.	Indianapolis	1:55 A.M.	4 h 11 min
Indianapolis	10:32 A.M.	Columbus	2:56 P.M.	4 h 24 min
Columbus	9:20 A.M.	Washington	3:40 P.M.	6 h 20 min
Washington	10:50 A.M.	New York City	2:18 P.M.	3 h 28 min

Name _____ Date _____

Using a Calendar

Write important dates and reminders on your calendars.

Month:

Sunday	Monday	Tuesday	Wednesday	Thursday	Friday	Saturday

Month:

Sunday	Monday	Tuesday	Wednesday	Thursday	Friday	Saturday

Month:

Sunday	Monday	Tuesday	Wednesday	Thursday	Friday	Saturday

10.16 PRACTICE

Problem Solving: **Using Strategies**

The graphs below record the height of 2 children from birth to one year. Use the graphs to answer each question.

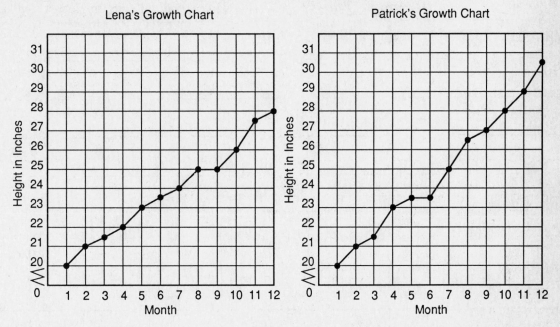

Lena's Growth Chart   Patrick's Growth Chart

1. At the beginning of the 5th month, how tall was Lena?
   How tall was Patrick?

   Lena was 23 inches. Patrick was $23\frac{1}{2}$ inches.

2. During which months were both children the same height?
   the 1st, 2nd, 3rd, and 6th months

3. Which child was taller at the beginning of the 7th month?
   At the beginning of the 10th month?
   Patrick was taller at both times.

4. How much did each child grow from the 1st month to the
   9th month?
   Lena grew 5 inches. Patrick grew 7 inches.

5. During which months did Lena grow the most? The least?
   She grew the most in the 10th month and the least in the 8th month.

11.1 PRACTICE/RECORDING SHEET for pages 338–339

Exploring Tenths

Answers may be in any order.

Less Than One Half Shaded		Exactly One Half Shaded		More Than One Half Shaded	
Words	**Decimal**	**Words**	**Decimal**	**Words**	**Decimal**
5. three tenths	0.3	five tenths	0.5	six tenths	0.6
one tenth	0.1			seven tenths	0.7
two tenths	0.2			eight tenths	0.8
four tenths	0.4			nine tenths	0.9

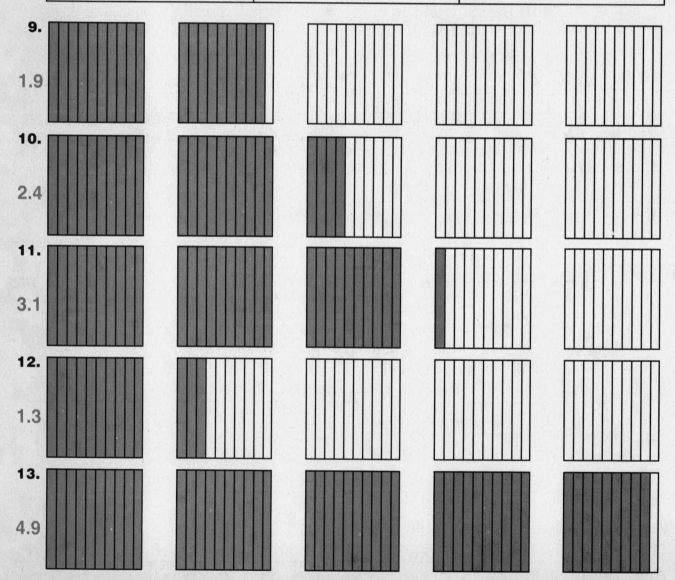

9. 1.9

10. 2.4

11. 3.1

12. 1.3

13. 4.9

11.2 **PRACTICE/RECORDING SHEET** for pages 340–341

Exploring Tenths and Hundredths

7.

Decimal	Greater or Less Than One Half?
0.75	greater than
0.25	less than
0.95	greater than
0.45	less than
0.50	equal to

8.

Pair 1

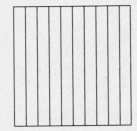 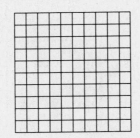

_____ _____

Pair 2

_____ _____

9.

Red Square	Green Square	Compare
0.6	0.25	0.6 > 0.25
0.5	0.05	0.5 > 0.05
0.5	0.55	0.55 > 0.5
0.3	0.30	0.3 = 0.30
0.8	0.75	0.8 < 0.75

11.3 ▸ PRACTICE

Place Value and Decimals

Write each decimal in the place-value chart.

1. one hundred twenty-seven and four tenths

hundreds	tens	ones	tenths	hundredths
1	2	7	4	

2. sixty-three hundredths

hundreds	tens	ones	tenths	hundredths
		0	6	3

3. five and eight tenths

hundreds	tens	ones	tenths	hundredths
		5	8	

4. twenty-three and seven hundredths

hundreds	tens	ones	tenths	hundredths
	2	3	0	7

5. three hundred and one tenth

hundreds	tens	ones	tenths	hundredths
3	0	0	1	

6. five tenths

hundreds	tens	ones	tenths	hundredths
		0	5	

11.4 PRACTICE   for pages 344–345

Comparing Decimals

Complete. Write <, >, or =. Then shade in the shapes that do not have equal decimals. The parts that have been shaded will answer the riddle.

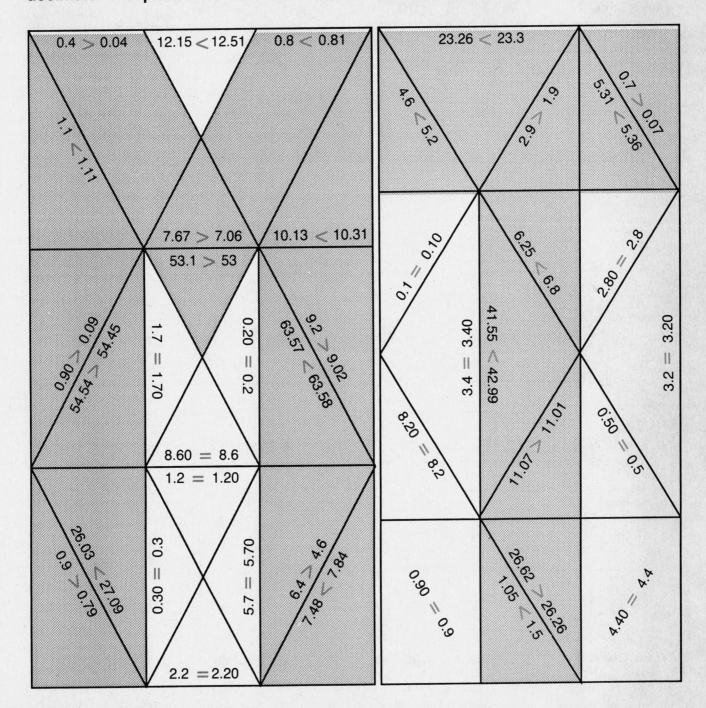

0.4 > 0.04   12.15 < 12.51   0.8 < 0.81

1.1 < 1.11

7.67 > 7.06   10.13 < 10.31

53.1 > 53

0.90 > 0.09

54.54 > 54.45

1.7 = 1.70

0.20 = 0.2

9.2 > 9.02

63.57 < 63.58

8.60 = 8.6

1.2 = 1.20

26.03

0.9 > 0.79

0.9 < 27.09

0.30 = 0.3

5.7 = 5.7

6.4 > 4.6

7.48 < 7.84

2.2 = 2.20

23.26 < 23.3

4.6 < 5.2

2.9 > 1.9

5.31 < 5.36

0.7 > 0.07

0.1 = 0.10

6.25 < 6.8

2.80 = 2.8

41.55 < 42.99

3.4 = 3.40

11.07 < 11.01

3.2 = 3.20

0.50 = 0.5

8.20 = 8.2

0.90 = 0.9

26.62 > 26.26

1.05 < 1.5

4.40 = 4.4

What are the initials of the first female British prime minister?

___M___   ___T___

11.5 PRACTICE

Ordering Decimals

Write the decimals in order, from least to greatest. Write your answers in the boxes. Below each answer, write the letter of the greatest decimal.

1. 3.6 A   3.07 R   3.19 T

3.07	3.19	3.6

_____ A _____

2. 0.09 F   9.9 L   9.19 S

0.09	9.19	9.9

_____ L _____

3. 7.8 J   78.8 P   7.88 Y

7.8	7.88	78.8

_____ P _____

4. 8.1 M   8.02 I   8.21 H

8.02	8.1	8.21

_____ H _____

5. 31.07 T   31.27 A   31.12 Q

31.07	31.12	31.27

_____ A _____

6. 0.93 B   0.11 V   0.08 U

0.08	0.11	0.93

_____ B _____

7. 0.47 E   0.4 L   0.04 A

0.04	0.4	0.47

_____ E _____

8. 7.2 W   7.18 D   7.23 T

7.18	7.2	7.23

_____ T _____

9. 1.38 S   1.27 H   1.2 Y

1.2	1.27	1.38

_____ S _____

10. 5.72 O   5.07 G   5.12 I

5.07	5.12	5.72

_____ O _____

11. 0.7 U   0.17 N   0.01 R

0.01	0.17	0.7

_____ U _____

12. 27.4 T   27.42 P   27.06 E

27.06	27.4	27.42

_____ P _____

Write the letter of the greatest decimal in each exercise on the line below. The letters will answer the riddle.

What has 26 letters but no envelopes?

A	L	P	H	A	B	E	T		S	O	U	P
1	2	3	4	5	6	7	8		9	10	11	12

Name _____   Date _____

11.6 PRACTICE   for pages 348–349

Problem Solving: Using Strategies

Solve each problem. Use one of the strategies you have learned.

Some of the students in Mr. Hubbard's class belong to a walking club. Club members keep a record of how far they walk each week.

Walk-a-Plenty Club
First Week

Name	Miles Walked
Karen	24.6
Seth	23.9
Blake	22.6
Ariel	21.9
Dana	20.9
Peter	20.1
Leon	19.8

Walk-a-Plenty Club
Second Week

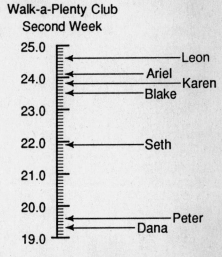

1. Which club members walked more than 22 miles the first week?
   Blake, Seth, and Karen

2. Which club members walked more than 22 miles the second week?
   Blake, Karen, Ariel and Leon

3. Sandra, another club member, walked 21.6 miles the first week. If her name had been listed in the table, between which 2 members would it appear?
   between Ariel and Dana

4. In which week did Blake walk more miles, the first week or the second week?
   the second week

5. How many of the members listed in the table walked between 21 and 23 miles the first week?
   2 of the members

6. How many of the members listed walked between 22 and 25 miles the second week?
   4 of the members

7. How many miles did each of the following members walk the second week?
   a. Dana ___19.3___   b. Leon ___24.6___   c. Seth ___21.9___
   d. Karen ___23.8___   e. Ariel ___24.1___

8. Which of the members walked a total distance that was closest to 20 miles during the first week? ___Peter___

© D.C. Heath and Company   (4) **145**

11.7 ▸PRACTICE

for page 350

Choose a Computation Method: Calculator or Mental Math

Write each answer. Write whether you used a calculator to find your answer. Choices may vary; possible choices are given.

1. $\frac{1}{3} + \frac{1}{3}$ $\frac{2}{3}$; no

2. $\begin{array}{r} 225 \\ +500 \\ \hline 725 \end{array}$; no

3. $\begin{array}{r} \$1.69 \\ +\ 7.87 \\ \hline \$9.56 \end{array}$; yes

4. $\begin{array}{r} 8532 \\ +3579 \\ \hline 12{,}111 \end{array}$; yes

5. $\begin{array}{r} 4070 \\ -596 \\ \hline 3474 \end{array}$; yes

6. $\begin{array}{r} 79 \\ \times 10 \\ \hline 790 \end{array}$; no

7. $\begin{array}{r} \$81.75 \\ -\ 78.75 \\ \hline \$\ 3.00 \end{array}$; no

8. $\begin{array}{r} 75 \\ +25 \\ \hline 100 \end{array}$; no

9. $\begin{array}{r} 362 \\ \times\ \ 5 \\ \hline 1810 \end{array}$; yes

10. $\begin{array}{r} 3871 \\ 5924 \\ +\ 419 \\ \hline 10{,}214 \end{array}$; yes

11. $\frac{3}{4} - \frac{1}{4}$ $\frac{1}{2}$; no

12. $\begin{array}{r} 105 \\ +500 \\ \hline 605 \end{array}$; no

13. $\begin{array}{r} \$3.55 \\ \times\ \ \ 8 \\ \hline \$28.40 \end{array}$; yes

14. $\begin{array}{r} 600 \\ \times\ \ 7 \\ \hline 4200 \end{array}$; no

15. $\begin{array}{r} 2798 \\ +3847 \\ \hline 6645 \end{array}$; yes

16. $\begin{array}{r} 7645 \\ -5286 \\ \hline 2359 \end{array}$; yes

17. $88 \div 8 =$ ___11; no___

18. $9 \times 30 =$ ___270; no___

19. $152 - 60 =$ ___92; yes___

20. $5 + 3 + 8 + 9 =$ ___25; no___

21. $6478 + 399 =$ ___6877; yes___

22. $450 \div 9 =$ ___50; no___

23. $176 - 7 =$ ___169; no___

24. $3 \times 437 =$ ___1311; yes___

25. Randy does yard work after school. On Monday he earned $3.25; on Tuesday he earned $2.00; on Wednesday he earned $3.75; and on Friday he earned $6.50. How much did he earn in all? ___$15.50; no___

26. Angie bought a pair of running shoes that cost $47.28. She gave the clerk $50.00. How much change did she get? ___$2.72, yes___

27. How do you decide when to use mental math?
___Answers may vary.___

11.8 PRACTICE

Using Rounding to Estimate

Round to the nearest whole number. Write the estimate. Draw a number line when it helps.

1. 8.7
    +6.1
    ‾‾‾‾
    15

2. 3.86
    +7.81
    ‾‾‾‾‾
    12

3. 7.1
    −3.9
    ‾‾‾‾
    3

4. 2.7
    +8.4
    ‾‾‾‾
    11

5. 5.25
    −2.10
    ‾‾‾‾‾
    3

6. 6.80
    +1.75
    ‾‾‾‾‾
    9

7. 6.4
    −0.9
    ‾‾‾‾
    5

8. 6.50
    −5.05
    ‾‾‾‾‾
    2

9. 3.8
    +9.7
    ‾‾‾‾
    14

10. 8.6
    +3.8
    ‾‾‾‾
    13

Circle the above answers in the maze below. Connect the answers to find the path from the outer circle to the center. Begin in the outer circle.

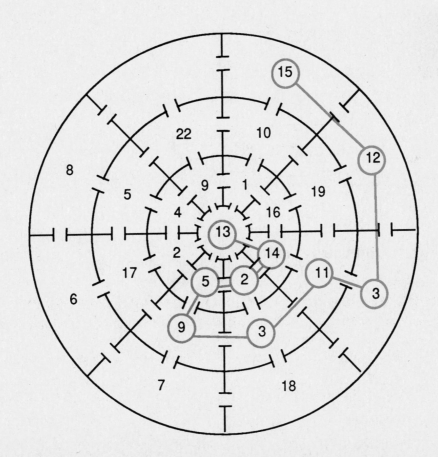

11.9 ▸ PRACTICE

Adding Decimals

Write the sum. Then use a ruler to draw a line from the dot by the sum to the dot beside the same decimal at the right. The letters you do not cross out will spell the answer to the riddle below.

1. $17.2 + 5.73$ _22.93_

2. $16.45 + 12.77$ _29.22_

3. $8.59 + 10.4 + 9.43$ _28.42_

4. $12.06 + 16.42$ _28.48_

5. $\$17.35 + \$8.85$ _$26.20_

6. $9.52 + 8.4 + 7.06$ _24.98_

7. $23.21 + 4.35 + 2.97$ _30.53_

8. $9.06 + 17.62 + 1.1$ _27.78_

9. $\$19.60 + \$9.32$ _$28.92_

10. $13.05 + 13.26$ _26.31_

Right-side dots: 28.42, 30.53, $26.20, 26.31, 27.78, $28.92, 29.22, 22.93, 28.48, 24.98

Letters: M U O T L J T K I W M P L O L I A E B R T S Q

What kind of pliers do you use in math?

M U L T I P L I E R S

11.10 PRACTICE

Subtracting Decimals

The subtracting machine subtracts a decimal from each number that is put in.
Write the answer in the Out Box.

1. In | Out
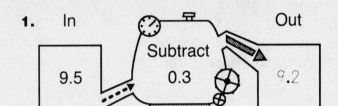

Subtract 0.3 — 9.5 → 9.2

2. In | Out
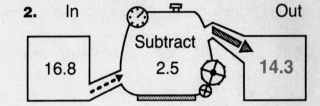

Subtract 2.5 — 16.8 → 14.3

3. In | Out
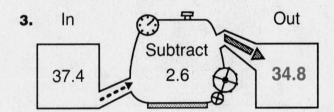

Subtract 2.6 — 37.4 → 34.8

4. In | Out
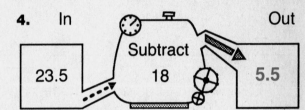

Subtract 18 — 23.5 → 5.5

5. In | Out
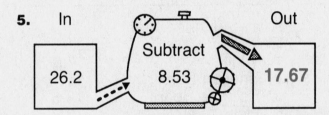

Subtract 8.53 — 26.2 → 17.67

6. In | Out
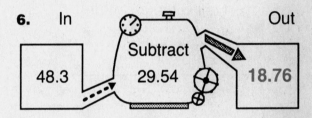

Subtract 29.54 — 48.3 → 18.76

7. In | Out
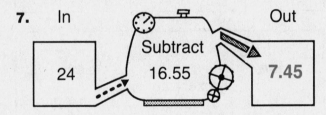

Subtract 16.55 — 24 → 7.45

8. In | Out
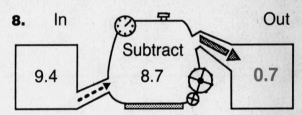

Subtract 8.7 — 9.4 → 0.7

9. In | Out
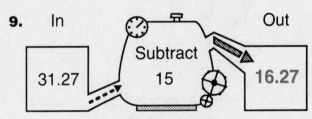

Subtract 15 — 31.27 → 16.27

10. In | Out
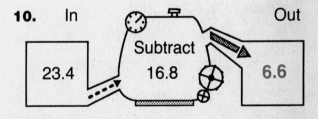

Subtract 16.8 — 23.4 → 6.6

11. In | Out
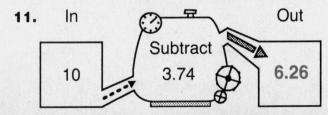

Subtract 3.74 — 10 → 6.26

12. In | Out
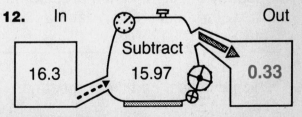

Subtract 15.97 — 16.3 → 0.33

11.11 PRACTICE

Using Decimals

The scorecards below show the scores that 3 gymnasts earned in a meet. There are 4 gymnastics events. The gymnasts performed these events in a different order. Each gymnast performed the event twice to get the score shown. The winning gymnast scored the most points for all 4 events combined.

Use pencil and paper, calculator, or mental math to answer each question.

1. Did Jean Yang earn a higher score for her first two events or her last two events?

for her first 2 events

Name: Jean Yang	
Event	Score
1. Unven Bars	18.6
2. Balance Beam	18.8
3. Floor Exercise	19.1
4. Vault	18.2

2. Which gymnast earned the highest total score for all the events? How can you tell without computing?

Alanna Miller; Answers may

vary but may include: by

mental math, by comparing

Name: Alanna Miller	
Event	Score
1. Vault	18.5
2. Uneven Bars	19.1
3. Balance Beam	18.8
4. Floor Exercise	19.2

3. After 3 events, which gymnast was in the lead?

Jean Yang

Name: Vera Lopez	
Event	Score
1. Floor Exercise	18.7
2. Vault	18.2
3. Uneven Bars	17.9
4. Balance Beam	18.9

4. What was the difference between Vera's total score and Jean's total score?

1.0

5. These 3 gymnasts are the highest scorers on their team. After the first event, the 3 best gymnasts on another team had a combined score of 54.9. Was Jean's team or the other team leading at that time?

Jean's team was leading.

6. Which gymnast had the highest combined score for the beam and the floor exercise?

Alanna

11.12 PRACTICE

Problem Solving: Using Math Sense

Solve each problem.

1. Dee wanted to buy a snack at the gymnastics meet. She reached into her pocket and found 3 small coins, which must have been pennies or dimes, and 3 larger coins, which must have been nickels or quarters. What is the most money Dee could have had? What is the least?

$1.05 is the most; $0.18 is

the least.

2. At the meet, Kevin received 20 votes for Most Outstanding Gymnast. Ivan received $\frac{1}{3}$ of the total votes. Susan got the remaining 6 votes. What can you tell about how many total votes there were?

There were 39 total votes.

3. Edna, Frank, and Suneeda agreed to share a 24-ounce bottle of water. Edna drank $\frac{2}{3}$ of the bottle and Suneeda drank 6 ounces. What can you tell about how much Frank drank?

Frank drank 2 ounces.

4. Suneeda trained for the meet by running 27 miles each week. She ran along a course that is 4.5 miles long. What can you tell about the number of days Suneeda trained each week?

Suneeda trained 6 days

each week.

5. Some numbers are missing from the scoreboard. What can you tell about the total number of points Hampshire scored in tumbling and parallel bars?

The total number was

8 points

Eton–Hampshire Gymnastics Meet					
School	Balance Beam	Parallel Bars	Tumbling	Rings	Totals
Eton	7.8	?	10	6.9	28.3
Hampshire	8.8	?	?	9.6	26.4

6. Eton won the gymnastics meet. What can you tell about the number of points Eton scored on the parallel bars?

Eton scored 3.6 points.

11.13 PRACTICE

for page 362

Estimating with Money

Write the estimate. Use any method you wish. Answers may vary.

1. $4.22 5.67 +4.60 $14.50	**2.** $2.98 1.60 +2.12 $7.00	**3.** $7.65 2.10 +9.52 $20.00	**4.** $1.90 6.12 +4.38 $12.40
5. $7.88 3.13 9.40 +4.55 $25.00	**6.** $5.55 9.80 8.99 +3.90 $28.50	**7.** $1.20 7.67 2.33 +4.77 $16.00	**8.** $9.07 2.10 7.42 +8.65 $27.00
9. $8.65 3.11 +2.91 $14.90	**10.** $4.45 7.80 +9.81 $23.00	**11.** $6.86 2.21 +2.33 $11.40	**12.** $8.77 6.83 +4.37 $20.00
13. $7.76 5.21 2.34 +1.59 $17.00	**14.** $5.67 8.88 8.67 +2.09 $25.40	**15.** $7.88 7.62 8.36 +4.07 $28.00	**16.** $1.11 3.68 1.42 +1.60 $8.00
17. $2.84 1.87 2.77 +2.79 $10.30	**18.** $5.09 2.82 4.92 +4.91 $18.00	**19.** $2.09 1.57 6.66 +2.09 $12.50	**20.** $4.08 4.80 7.12 +5.55 $21.60
21. $9.10 4.33 7.99 +1.99 $23.40	**22.** $5.29 1.11 6.42 +8.41 $21.20	**23.** $7.11 8.21 3.98 +2.65 $22.00	**24.** $1.70 9.98 2.21 +4.87 $19.00

(4) **152**

12.1 PRACTICE

Using Patterns

Circle the correct product below each exercise. Use mental math. Then use the products to trace two paths. Help the king and the queen go from the forest to the castle.

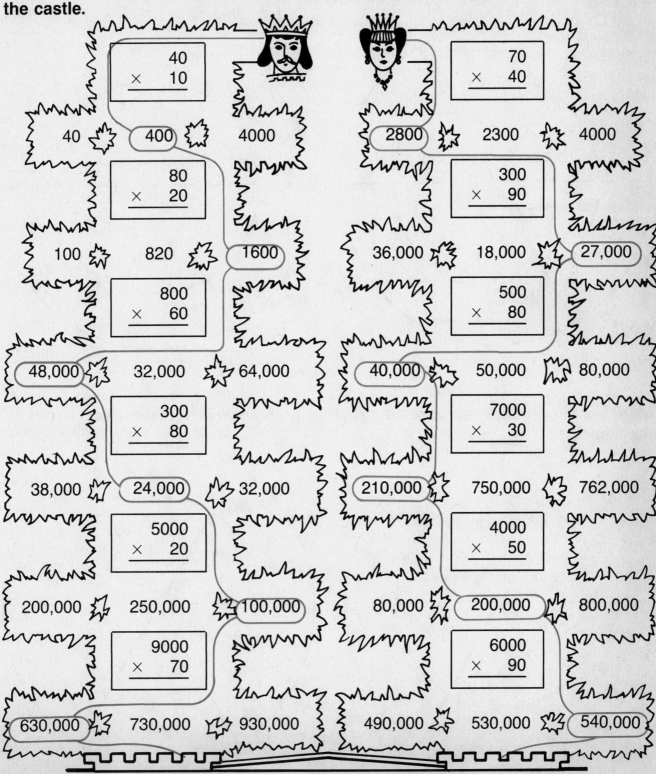

$$\begin{array}{r} 40 \\ \times\ 10 \\ \hline \end{array}$$

40   400   4000

$$\begin{array}{r} 80 \\ \times\ 20 \\ \hline \end{array}$$

100   820   1600

$$\begin{array}{r} 800 \\ \times\ 60 \\ \hline \end{array}$$

48,000   32,000   64,000

$$\begin{array}{r} 300 \\ \times\ 80 \\ \hline \end{array}$$

38,000   24,000   32,000

$$\begin{array}{r} 5000 \\ \times\ 20 \\ \hline \end{array}$$

200,000   250,000   100,000

$$\begin{array}{r} 9000 \\ \times\ 70 \\ \hline \end{array}$$

630,000   730,000   930,000

$$\begin{array}{r} 70 \\ \times\ 40 \\ \hline \end{array}$$

2800   2300   4000

$$\begin{array}{r} 300 \\ \times\ 90 \\ \hline \end{array}$$

36,000   18,000   27,000

$$\begin{array}{r} 500 \\ \times\ 80 \\ \hline \end{array}$$

40,000   50,000   80,000

$$\begin{array}{r} 7000 \\ \times\ 30 \\ \hline \end{array}$$

210,000   750,000   762,000

$$\begin{array}{r} 4000 \\ \times\ 50 \\ \hline \end{array}$$

80,000   200,000   800,000

$$\begin{array}{r} 6000 \\ \times\ 90 \\ \hline \end{array}$$

490,000   530,000   540,000

12.2 PRACTICE

for pages 372–373

Estimating Products

Estimate the product using front-end estimation. Write each answer in the correct part of the wheel.

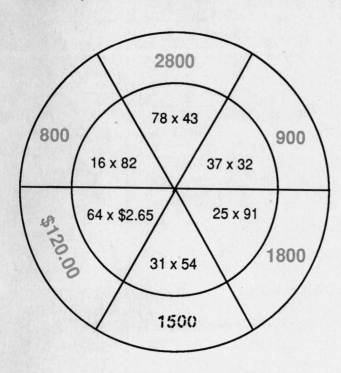

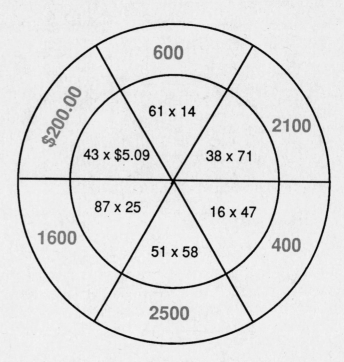

Estimate the product using rounding. Write each answer in the correct part of the wheel.

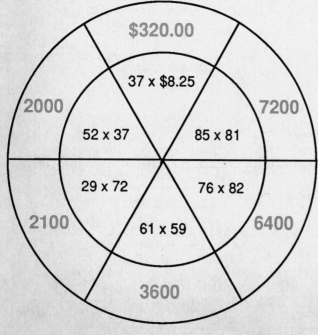

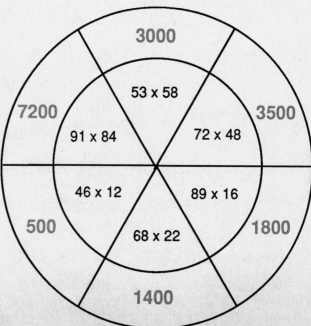

12.3 PRACTICE

Multiplying by Multiples of Ten

Write the letter of the most reasonable estimate.

1. $70 \times 269 =$ __b__
   a. 2100
   b. 21,000
   c. 210,000

2. $51 \times 80 =$ __b__
   a. 400
   b. 4000
   c. 40,000

3. $385 \times 20 =$ __b__
   a. 800
   b. 8000
   c. 80,000

4. $824 \times 30 =$ __a__
   a. 24,000
   b. 240,000
   c. 2,400,000

5. $40 \times 62 =$ __a__
   a. 2400
   b. 24,000
   c. 240,000

6. $780 \times 70 =$ __c__
   a. 560
   b. 5600
   c. 56,000

Estimate. Then write the product.

7.
$$\begin{array}{r} 236 \\ \times\ 50 \\ \hline 11{,}800 \end{array}$$

8.
$$\begin{array}{r} 362 \\ \times\ 30 \\ \hline 10{,}860 \end{array}$$

9.
$$\begin{array}{r} 45 \\ \times\ 40 \\ \hline 1800 \end{array}$$

10.
$$\begin{array}{r} 62 \\ \times\ 20 \\ \hline 1240 \end{array}$$

11.
$$\begin{array}{r} 124 \\ \times\ 60 \\ \hline 7440 \end{array}$$

12.
$$\begin{array}{r} 35 \\ \times\ 30 \\ \hline 1050 \end{array}$$

13.
$$\begin{array}{r} 478 \\ \times\ 10 \\ \hline 4780 \end{array}$$

14.
$$\begin{array}{r} 77 \\ \times\ 70 \\ \hline 5390 \end{array}$$

15.
$$\begin{array}{r} 638 \\ \times\ 80 \\ \hline 51{,}040 \end{array}$$

16.
$$\begin{array}{r} 283 \\ \times\ 20 \\ \hline 5660 \end{array}$$

17.
$$\begin{array}{r} 52 \\ \times\ 70 \\ \hline 3640 \end{array}$$

18.
$$\begin{array}{r} 98 \\ \times\ 60 \\ \hline 5880 \end{array}$$

Solve.

19. Mrs. Rock was ordering pencils for the school. She wanted to order 60 pencils for each class. There were 23 classes in the school. How many pencils should she have ordered? _____ **1380 pencils** _____

20. Mrs. Espinoza and Mrs. Moya took their students to the museum. Each of the 45 students had to pay $0.90 to help pay for the trip. How much money did the students contribute toward the trip? _____ **$40.50** _____

◢12.4◤ PRACTICE
for pages 376–377

Problem Solving: Using Strategies

Solve each problem. You may want to use centimeter squared paper.

1. Kendra is planning a rectangular panel for a kitchen wall in a home.
   a. How many square tiles will be needed for the panel?

   12

   b. What is the area of each square?

   64 square inches

   c. What is the area of the panel?

   768 square inches

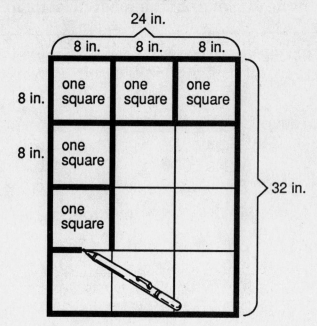

2. To make a tile panel for the wall of a new restaurant, Kendra considers using tiles that are 1 foot by 1 foot. The owner wants an area of 80 square feet tiled.
   a. How many tiles will be needed?

   80 tiles will be needed.

   b. How might the tiles be arranged to make a rectangle?

   Answers may vary but may include: 1 × 80; 2 × 40; 5 × 16; 8 × 10

3. The restaurant owner wants a tile border to go around the perimeter of the 80 square feet of wall panel. How many feet of tile border will be needed to frame the panel?

   Answers will vary but may include: 36 ft; 42 ft; 48 ft; 84 ft; 162 ft.

4. Kendra decides to make the restaurant's panel from 8-inch by 8-inch tiles.
   a. How many tiles will she need for the panel?

   180 tiles

   b. Will Kendra need to increase the size of the border? Why or why not?

   No, the border will still frame the same area.

Name _____ Date _____

12.5 PRACTICE

for pages 378–379

Multiplying with Array Diagrams

Write the multiplication sentence in each section of the array diagram. Then write the product.

1.
$$\begin{array}{r} 21 \\ \times\ 34 \\ \hline 4 \leftarrow 4 \times 1 \\ 80 \leftarrow 4 \times 20 \\ 30 \leftarrow 30 \times 1 \\ \underline{600} \leftarrow 30 \times 20 \\ 714 \end{array}$$

	20	1
30	30 × 20 = 600	30 × 1 = 30
4	4 × 20 = 80	4 × 1 = 4

2.
$$\begin{array}{r} 19 \\ \times\ 15 \\ \hline 45 \leftarrow 5 \times 9 \\ 50 \leftarrow 5 \times 10 \\ 90 \leftarrow 10 \times 9 \\ \underline{100} \leftarrow 10 \times 10 \\ 285 \end{array}$$

	10	9
10	10 × 10 = 100	10 × 9 = 90
5	5 × 10 = 50	5 × 9 = 45

3.
$$\begin{array}{r} 55 \\ \times\ 27 \\ \hline 1485 \end{array}$$

	50	5
20	20 × 50 = 1000	20 × 5 = 100
7	7 × 50 = 350	7 × 5 = 35

4.
$$\begin{array}{r} 92 \\ \times\ 13 \\ \hline 1196 \end{array}$$

	90	2
10	10 × 90 = 900	10 × 2 = 20
3	3 × 90 = 270	3 × 2 = 6

5.
$$\begin{array}{r} 38 \\ \times\ 46 \\ \hline 1748 \end{array}$$

	30	8
40	40 × 30 = 1200	40 × 8 = 320
6	6 × 30 = 180	6 × 8 = 48

6.
$$\begin{array}{r} 17 \\ \times\ 25 \\ \hline 425 \end{array}$$

	10	7
20	20 × 10 = 200	20 × 7 = 140
5	5 × 10 = 50	5 × 7 = 35

7.
$$\begin{array}{r} 12 \\ \times\ 29 \\ \hline 348 \end{array}$$

	10	2
20	20 × 10 = 200	20 × 2 = 40
9	9 × 10 = 90	9 × 2 = 18

8.
$$\begin{array}{r} 56 \\ \times\ 73 \\ \hline 4088 \end{array}$$

	50	6
70	70 × 50 = 3500	70 × 6 = 420
3	3 × 50 = 150	3 × 6 = 18

12.6 PRACTICE

Multiplying 2-Digit Numbers

Write the product.

1. 34 D $\times 23$ 782	**2.** 18 B $\times 11$ 198	**3.** 56 O $\times 32$ 1792	**4.** 42 N $\times 12$ 504
5. 64 E $\times 55$ 3520	**6.** 43 T $\times 81$ 3483	**7.** 72 L $\times 63$ 4536	**8.** 19 A $\times 21$ 399
9. 94 T $\times 89$ 8366	**10.** 86 I $\times 75$ 6450	**11.** 79 T $\times 64$ 5056	**12.** 98 U $\times 62$ 6076
13. 31 B $\times 49$ 1519	**14.** 95 E $\times 35$ 3325	**15.** 88 R $\times 43$ 3784	**16.** 65 G $\times 38$ 2470
17. 25 C $\times 82$ 2050	**18.** 77 F $\times 16$ 1232	**19.** 94 V $\times 32$ 3008	**20.** 62 M $\times 18$ 1116

Use the products to find the important message.

D	O	N	'	T		B	E		A
782	1792	504		3483		198	3520		399

L	I	T	T	E	R		B	U	G
4536	6450	5056	8366	3325	3784		1519	6076	2470

12.7 PRACTICE

Logical Reasoning

Look at each group of multiplication examples. Then complete each statement about the group by writing *All, Some,* or *None* on the line.

34	15	57	84	68
× 12	× 6	× 10	× 45	× 6
408	90	570	3780	408

1. ____**Some**____ of the examples have 6 as a factor.

2. ____**None**____ of the examples have a 3-digit factor.

3. ____**All**____ of the products have a zero.

4. ____**Some**____ of the examples have a 1-digit factor.

61	274	48	9431	27
× 4	× 16	× 12	× 6	× 22
244	4384	576	56,586	594

5. ____**All**____ of the products are even numbers.

6. ____**None**____ of the examples show the multiplication of money.

7. ____**Some**____ of the products contain a 5.

8. ____**Some**____ of the examples have the same number of digits in their 2 factors.

300	50	6000	80	20
× 4	× 7	× 9	× 6	× 8
1200	350	54,000	480	160

9. ____**All**____ of the examples can be done with mental math.

10. ____**None**____ of the examples have a 2-digit multiplier.

11. ____**All**____ of the products are even.

12.8 ▷ PRACTICE   for pages 384–385

Multiplying 3-Digit Numbers

Multiply. Use the products to complete the crossnumber puzzle.

A 3	B 3	C 4	D 7	E 2	■	F 4	G 8	H 2	I 4
J 3	6	2	1	6	■	K 7	2	0	8
L 6	2	■	M 2	2	N 9	5	2	■	3
P 6	6	■	Q 8	4	8	■		R 1	6
■		S 4		■	T 5	U 3	V 5	5	■
W 2	X 7	2	Y 8	■	Z 8	3	6	2	AA 8
BB 1	4	6	1	CC 6	■	DD 1	8	■	1
EE 4	2	■		3	■	FF 2	1	■	8
GG 9	5	6	1	6	■	■		HH 5	1

Across

- **A.** 523 × 64
- **F.** 804 × 6
- **J.** 503 × 72
- **K.** 901 × 8
- **L.** 31 × 2
- **M.** 604 × 38
- **P.** 33 × 2
- **Q.** 424 × 2
- **R.** 4 × 4
- **T.** 63 × 85
- **W.** 44 × 62
- **Z.** 909 × 92
- **BB.** 406 × 36
- **DD.** 3 × 6
- **EE.** 6 × 7
- **FF.** 3 × 7
- **GG.** 996 × 96
- **HH.** 17 × 3

Down

- **A.** 66 × 51
- **B.** 74 × 49
- **C.** 7 × 6
- **D.** 66 × 108
- **E.** 328 × 8
- **F.** 95 × 5
- **G.** 411 × 2
- **H.** 4 × 5
- **I.** 62 × 78
- **N.** 318 × 31
- **R.** 38 × 4
- **S.** 6 × 71
- **U.** 138 × 24
- **V.** 299 × 19
- **W.** 307 × 7
- **X.** 825 × 9
- **Y.** 9 × 9
- **AA.** 909 × 9
- **CC.** 212 × 3

Name _____ Date _____

Multiplying Money

Answers will vary.

Quantity	Item No.	Type of Flower	Color	Unit Price	Total
				Grand Total	

12.10 PRACTICE for pages 388–389

Multiplying Three Factors

The rule of counting zeros when multiplying multiples of ten can be used for finding products of more than two factors. For example: $50 \times 60 \times 20$

Step 1: Multiply the non-zero numbers. $5 \times 6 \times 2 = 60$

Step 2: Count and write the zeros. $5\underline{0} \times 6\underline{0} \times 2\underline{0} = 60,\underline{000}$

Write the product.

1. $70 \times 30 \times 40 =$ _____ 84,000 _____   **2.** $50 \times 10 \times 80 =$ _____ 40,000 _____

3. $60 \times 40 \times 20 =$ _____ 48,000 _____   **4.** $90 \times 40 \times 20 =$ _____ 72,000 _____

5. $40 \times 60 \times 40 =$ _____ 96,000 _____   **6.** $80 \times 30 \times 20 =$ _____ 48,000 _____

7. $70 \times 4 \times 30 =$ _____ 8400 _____   **8.** $50 \times 30 \times 6 =$ _____ 9000 _____

9. $20 \times 40 \times 70 =$ _____ 56,000 _____   **10.** $20 \times 50 \times 5 =$ _____ 5000 _____

11. $3 \times 80 \times 30 =$ _____ 7200 _____   **12.** $90 \times 20 \times 10 =$ _____ 18,000 _____

13. $700 \times 20 \times 7 =$ _____ 98,000 _____   **14.** $20 \times 6 \times 60 =$ _____ 7200 _____

Write the product.

15. $90 \times 60 \times 40 =$ _____ 216,000 _____   **16.** $60 \times 40 \times 70 =$ _____ 168,000 _____

17. $50 \times 40 \times 70 =$ _____ 140,000 _____   **18.** $80 \times 20 \times 90 =$ _____ 144,000 _____

19. $70 \times 30 \times 80 =$ _____ 168,000 _____   **20.** $60 \times 70 \times 80 =$ _____ 336,000 _____

21. $50 \times 90 \times 700 =$ _____ 3,150,000 _____   **22.** $6000 \times 80 \times 50 =$ _____ 24,000,000 _____

23. $40 \times 700 \times 90 =$ _____ 2,520,000 _____   **24.** $800 \times 90 \times 70 =$ _____ 5,040,000 _____

25. $70 \times 30 \times 900 =$ _____ 1,890,000 _____   **26.** $9 \times 800 \times 40 =$ _____ 288,000 _____

(4) **162**

12.11 PRACTICE

Problem Solving: Using Math Sense

Solve each problem. Explain how you got your answer.

1. At which store does 5 pounds of rice cost less?

   La Perla
   _____

La Perla 1 lb of rice 69¢	El Pato 5 lb of rice $3.59

2. Lita has a five-dollar bill. Is that enough to buy 10 pounds of rice?

   no
   _____

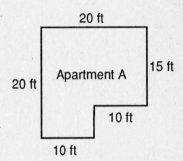

3. Lorna is supposed to be in Fairfield at 10:00 A.M. The express train takes 2 hours, but the last express leaves at 7:45 A.M. After that, the local train leaves every half hour and takes 2 hours and 20 minutes to reach Fairfield. What train should Lorna take in order to arrive on time?

   the 7:45 A.M. express
   _____

4. Richard is looking for an apartment. He sees two that he likes. He decides to take the apartment that has the greater area. Which apartment will he take?

   Apartment A
   _____

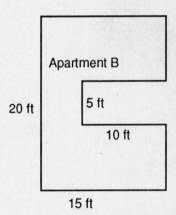

5. Both apartments need to be painted. Which apartment probably has more wall area to be painted?

   Apartment B
   _____

6. Are there more seconds in a day or hours in a week?

   more seconds in a day
   _____

7. On April 30, 1990, at 3:00 P.M., Sean received a gift—a dinosaur egg. The friend who gave him the gift said that the egg will hatch in exactly 1000 hours. On what date and at what time should Sean expect the egg to hatch?

   June 11 at 7:00 A.M.
   _____

13.1 ▸ PRACTICE

Using Patterns

Find your way through the maze. Connect the problems that have correct quotients to one another. Use mental math to solve each problem.

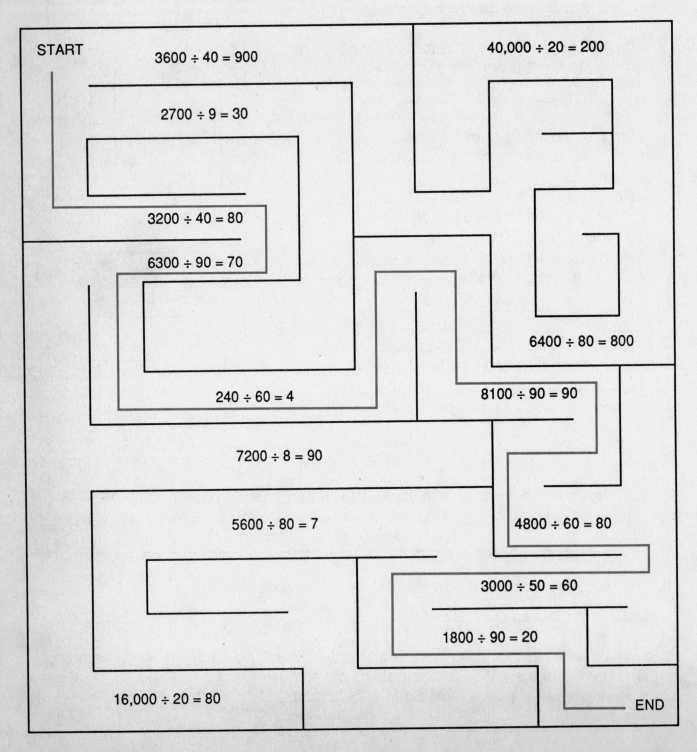

START

3600 ÷ 40 = 900

2700 ÷ 9 = 30

3200 ÷ 40 = 80

6300 ÷ 90 = 70

240 ÷ 60 = 4

7200 ÷ 8 = 90

5600 ÷ 80 = 7

16,000 ÷ 20 = 80

40,000 ÷ 20 = 200

6400 ÷ 80 = 800

8100 ÷ 90 = 90

4800 ÷ 60 = 80

3000 ÷ 50 = 60

1800 ÷ 90 = 20

END

Estimating Quotients

Circle the letter of the better estimate. Then circle the letter of the number the quotient is closer to.

1. 24)82
   The quotient is between   (L.) 3 and 4   W. 4 and 5
   The quotient is closer to   I. 5   (O.) 3

2. 32)565
   The quotient is between   L. 20 and 30   (O.) 10 and 20
   The quotient is closer to   (K.) 20   Y. 30

3. 1360 ÷ 14
   The quotient is between   T. 80 and 90   (O.) 90 and 100
   The quotient is closer to   P. 90   (U.) 100

4. 252 ÷ 31
   The quotient is between   (T.) 8 and 9   P. 9 and 10
   The quotient is closer to   (P.) 8   R. 10

5. 27)552
   The quotient is between   F. 30 and 40   (O.) 20 and 30
   The quotient is closer to   (I.) 20   A. 30

6. 359 ÷ 11
   The quotient is between   L. 40 and 50   (N.) 30 and 40
   The quotient is closer to   (T.) 30   L. 40

Where did the campers spend the night?

Write the letters you circled. Put an X on the map.

L   O   O   K   O   U   T

P   O   I   N   T

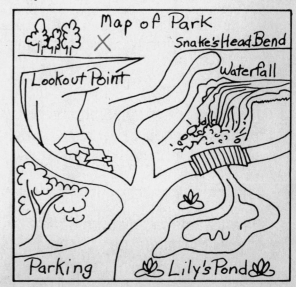

13.3 PRACTICE

Problem Solving: Using Strategies

Solve each problem. Use one of the strategies you have learned. Estimate when it helps you.

Shrimp, a slender shellfish, is a popular food. At Sal's Shrimp-by-the-Bucket, you can buy shrimp that are already cooked or you can buy shrimp and cook them yourself.

Sal's Shrimp-by-the-Bucket			
Bucket Size	Number of Shrimp per Bucket	Cost per bucket	
		We cook	You cook
small	10	$ 5.95	$ 4.95
medium	16	$ 8.95	$ 7.95
large	25	$12.95	$11.95
jumbo	36	$17.95	$16.95

1. Lazlo bought 1 bucket of each size already cooked.

   a. How many shrimp did he get? _____ **87 shrimp** _____

   b. How much did it cost him? _____ **$45.80** _____

   c. Could Lazlo have gotten that many cooked shrimp for

   less? How? _____ **2 jumbo, 1 medium for $44.85** _____

2. Dale plans to buy 3 dozen cooked shrimp. He wants to get the best buy he can.

   a. Do 2 medium buckets cost more than or less than 1

   jumbo bucket? _____ **less than** _____

   b. Which of the two buckets is the better buy? Why?

   Jumbo; for 5¢ more, you get 4 more shrimp.

3. June needs to buy 35 shrimp she will cook. Which bucket or buckets should she buy in order to spend the least amount of money? How much will she spend?

   1 large bucket and 1 small bucket for $16.90

4. Dawn wants to buy from 32 to 36 shrimp. What are the different combinations of containers she can buy?

   2 medium; 1 large and 1 small; 1 jumbo; 2 small, 1 medium

13.4 PRACTICE

One-Digit Quotients

Estimate. Then divide.

1.   8   F
   24)192

2.   5   E
   19)95

3.   7   T
   34)238

4.   9   H
   82)738

5.   6   O
   73)438

6.   7 R2   B
   56)394

7.   4 R1   T
   94)377

8.   8 R12   L
   64)524

9.   5 R14   O
   17)99

10.   9 R31   L
   85)796

11.   7 R44   A
   45)359

12.   7 R33   U
   78)579

13.   8 R17   I
   36)305

14.   6 R40   S
   51)346

15.   9 R11   T
   97)884

16.   5 R27   M
   63)342

17.   4 R27   D
   87)375

18.   9 R3   A
   74)669

Write the letter that matches each quotient to find the answer to the question.

Where would you go to watch the *Super Bowl*?

T	H	E
7	9	5

F	O	O	T	B	A	L	L
8	6	5 R14	4 R1	7 R2	7 R44	8 R12	9 R31

S	T	A	D	I	U	M
6 R40	9 R11	9 R3	4 R27	8 R17	7 R33	5 R27

◢ 13.5 ◢PRACTICE   for pages 406–407

··

Two-Digit Quotients

Estimate. Then divide.

1.   26
37)962

2.   16 R6
53)854

3.   34
29)986

4.   29 R16
24)712

5.   52 R10
19)998

6.   35 R19
27)964

7.   52 R1
18)937

8.   39 R18
23)915

9.   29 R30
32)958

10.   50 R12
17)862

11.   29 R23
29)864

12.   34 R11
26)895

Color the puzzle pieces that contain your answers. Then you will have the answer to the number of home runs Henry Aaron hit in his Major League baseball career.

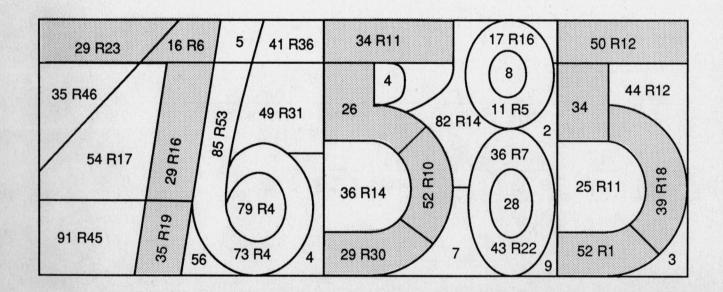

13.6 PRACTICE

Problem Solving: Using Strategies

Solve each problem. Use one of the strategies you have learned.

1. Luke found a summer job gardening. He gets paid $3.50 an hour. He works about 25 hours a week. How much does Luke make each week?

   $87.50 a week

2. Luke must weed a garden that measures 12 feet by 15 feet. It takes him 10 minutes to weed 1 square yard. How long will it take him to weed the garden? (HINT: 9 square feet = 1 square yard)

   3 hours and 20 minutes,

   or 200 minutes

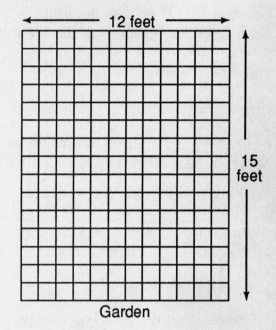

Garden

3. Sara found a summer job baby-sitting for a toddler. She works from 8:30 A.M. until 12:00 P.M. and then from 1:30 p.m. until 5:00 P.M. She works Monday through Friday.
   a. How many hours a week does Sara work?

   35 hours

   b. If Sara received $2.75 an hour, how much money would she make a week?

   $96.25

4. Reynold has a summer job delivering groceries. He works 6 hours a day and makes $2.50 an hour plus tips. He works 5 days a week. He usually delivers from 10 to 12 orders each day. He receives an average tip of $1 for each order he delivers. What is the most Reynold makes in a week? The least?

   most-$135; least-$125

5. Stan put up a poster to advertise odd jobs he wants to do. Last week he spent 3 hours mowing lawns, 2 hours trimming hedges, and 8 hours painting a fence. He also washed 26 windows. How much money did he earn?

   $140.00

STAN'S ODD JOBS	
Job	Charge
Window washing	$2.00 per window
Painting	$5.00 per hour
Lawn mowing	$10.00 per hour
Hedge trimming	$9.00 per hour

Name _____ Date _____

Using Division

Solve each problem.

1. Fairview Fun Park opens at 9:00 A.M. The Kahn family lives 170 miles from the park. They leave home at 6:30 in the morning and drive an average of 55 miles per hour. Will they arrive in time for the park opening? About how early or late will they be?

   No, they will arrive about a half hour late.

2. At the park, 86 people are waiting in line for the Moon Rocket ride. If each rocket holds 15 passengers, how many rockets would be needed for all the people waiting to ride at the same time? **6 rockets**

3. A booklet for rides costs $28.20 and contains 12 tickets. Individual tickets sell for $2.75 each. How much money can a person save per ticket by buying a booklet?

   40¢ per ticket

4. The distance from the park entrance to the Haunted Palace is 760 meters. Signs leading to the palace are located every 60 meters, starting at the entrance. Jamie entered the park and headed for the Haunted Palace. She passed 7 signs. Is she more than or less than halfway there? **more than halfway**

5. The Silver Streak Railroad circles the park once every 16 minutes. The railroad runs from 9:30 A.M. until 7:00 P.M., but it shuts down from 12 noon until 1:30. How many trips around the park does the Silver Streak make in a day?

   30 trips

6. The railroad has 11 cars. Each car has 8 seats. If 77 people get on the train and the same number of passengers sit in each car, how many empty seats will there be in each car? **one empty seat**

7. A 13-week pass to Fairview Fun Park costs $84.50. A 30-week pass costs $180. Which pass costs less per week? How much less?

   the 30-week pass; $.50 less per week

8. A regular box of souvenir crayons sells for $2.50 and contains 24 crayons. A jumbo box contains 40 crayons and sells for $4.99. Which box is a better buy?

   the regular box

13.8 PRACTICE

Using Division for Averages

Solve each problem. You may want to use a calculator.

To earn money for a trip to an All Star game, the Howling Hitters washed cars in their community. During the year, they kept a graph of the number of cars they washed each month.

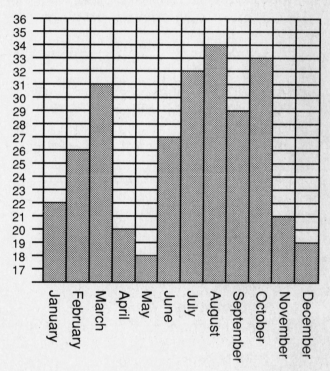

1. What was the average number of cars the team washed per month?

   26 cars

2. In how many months did they wash fewer cars than the average?

   5 months

3. What was the average number of cars they washed during the first 6 months of the year?

   24 cars

4. What was the average number of cars washed during the second half of the year?

   28 cars

Deanne kept track of the money she earned for the team.

5. What was the average amount of money Deanne earned per month?

   $35

6. Were Deanne's average monthly earnings higher in the first half of the year or in the second? How do you know?

   the second; higher total earnings

7. During which 2-month period were average earnings higher? How do you know?

   July–August;

   highest-earning months

Deanne's Car Wash Earnings

Month	Amount Earned
January	$36
February	$40
March	$32
April	$21
May	$39
June	$25
July	$54
August	$62
September	$27
October	$30
November	$32
December	$22

13.9 PRACTICE   for page 414

Problem Solving: **Using Strategies**

Solve each problem. Use one of the strategies you have learned.

1. Maizie's Frozen Yogurt Heaven offers a large dish of frozen yogurt with any 2 toppings for $2.75. They have 5 toppings to choose from: coconut, granola, walnuts, sprinkles, and strawberries. How many different combinations of 2 toppings are there? _____ **10 different combinations**

2. Santa's North Pole Delight offers any 3 toppings on their yogurt for $3.25. They also have the same five toppings to choose from: coconut, granola, walnuts, sprinkles, and strawberries. How many different combinations of 3 toppings are there? _____ **10 different combinations**

3. Su has $7.00 to buy yogurt for herself and 3 friends at Maizie's.
   a. What is the most expensive yogurt she can buy if she wants to spend the same amount of money for each dish of yogurt? _____ **plain, medium dish**
   b. How much more money does Su need to buy herself a medium with 3 toppings? _____ **60¢ more**

Maizie's Frozen Yogurt Heaven		
Dish	Plain	2 Toppings
Small	$1.25	$1.50
Medium	$1.75	$2.00
Large	$2.50	$2.75
Additional Toppings 35¢ each		

4. Mark is delivering dairy products to 4 stores in Henryville. If he entered Henryville from Hicks Street, what would be the best route he could take? Trace it on the map. (HINT: Streets are one-way.)
Answers may vary. One possible solution is shown.

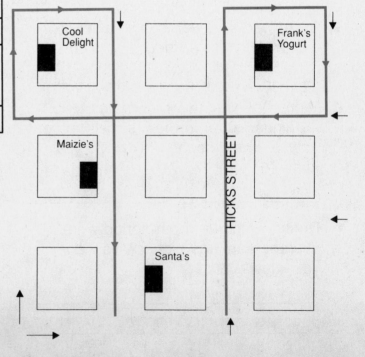

(4) **172**